Use of Maths for AQA

AQA Approved

Advanced Level

Decision Maths

Stan Dolan

OXFORD
UNIVERSITY PRESS

OXFORD
UNIVERSITY PRESS

Great Clarendon Street, Oxford OX2 6DP

Oxford University Press is a department of the University of Oxford. It furthers the University's objective of excellence in research, scholarship, and education by publishing worldwide in

Oxford New York

Auckland Cape Town Dar es Salaam Hong Kong Karachi
Kuala Lumpur Madrid Melbourne Mexico City Nairobi
New Delhi Shanghai Taipei Toronto

With offices in

Argentina Austria Brazil Chile Czech Republic France Greece Guatemala Hungary
Italy Japan Poland Portugal Singapore South Korea Switzerland Thailand Turkey
Ukraine Vietnam

© Oxford University Press 2013

The moral rights of the author have been asserted

Database right Oxford University Press (maker)

First published 2013

British Library Cataloguing in Publication Data

Data available

ISBN: 978-0-19-912994-2

10 9 8 7 6 5 4 3 2 1

Printed in Great Britain by Bell and Bain Ltd. Glasgow

MIX
Paper from
responsible sources
FSC
www.fsc.org   FSC® C007785

Acknowledgments

AQA examination questions are reproduced by permission of AQA Education (AQA). AQA accepts no responsibility for the accuracy or method of working in the answers given.
The publisher would like to thank the following for kind permission to reproduce photographs.

p4: Laguna Design/Science Photo Library; p4: Neftali/Shutterstoc.com; p16: © Interfoto/Alamy; p17: © Bettmann/ CORBIS; p20: Christian Lagerek/OUP; p36: © Interfoto/Alamy; p40: Pineasso/Shutterstock; p48: Hamilton Richards; p52: Dageldog/Istock; p64: Ninjamonkeystudio/Istock; p70: Zhukov Oleg/Shutterstock; p82: © Mary Evans Picture Library/Alamy; p88: S_Oleg/Shutterstock; p106: © Classic Image/Alamy.

Front cover illustration by Michael Levi.

The author would like to thank Marron Liqueurs with help providing data.

AQA AS Use of Maths: Decision Mathematics – Important information

Please note that when teaching the AQA AS Use of Maths course, you must refer to AQA's specification as your definitive source of information. While this book has been written to match AQA's specification, it cannot provide complete coverage of each unit (eg Decision Mathematics).

Contents

About this book

This book has been written for the Decision Mathematics module (9997) of the AQA Use of Mathematics A-level qualification (9361/2). Full details of the examination and specification can be found on the AQA website.

> http://web.aqa.org.uk/

A dedicated website for this book can be found at

> http://www.oxfordsecondary.co.uk./useofmaths

The author is an experienced teacher who has an excellent understanding of the AQA specification.

The start of each chapter introduces the main ideas to be covered and provides motivation for the material in the chapter. It contains two features.

Preparation

Identifies skills you should be able to demonstrate before you start this chapter.

A feature of Decision Mathematics is that it relies on very little prior mathematical knowledge. Preparation questions may therefore be designed to promote thinking about issues and not simply be a diagnostic test for material covered in earlier chapters.

Challenge

A problem based on a real-life scenario; the investigation and solution of which is designed to rely on using the material developed in the chapter.

The challenge allows for the possibility of a 'project' based approach to covering the material. Helped by teacher mediation, you will find the techniques necessary to solve a real-life problem in the chapter.

The sections in each chapter consist of explanatory text, examples and an exercise with progressive questions designed to consolidate the material just covered. The sections may contain a number of features.

p.1 ▶ Key points are highlighted

Key words are shown in bold.

p.4 ▶ Arrows in the margin give page reference to prior discussion or further development.

Comment boxes are used to provide additional information or comment.

2

Example

Questions highlight important ideas or are typical questions.

- - - - - - - - - - - - - - - - - -

Answers show how to apply appropriate techniques and layout your workings.

Algorithm

1 Clear, step-by-step instructions on how to carry out important algorithms

Each chapter also includes an Investigation section which provides a wider context and further directions in which to explore the material covered in the chapter. Opportunities to carry out research and investigate the use of ICT are highlighted. Each investigation also includes a suggestion for a project.

Project

An idea or a scenario which is designed to allow the material covered in the chapter to be developed into an extended activity.

At A2, Use of Mathematics contains a compulsory module, USE2, consisting of two projects. It is hoped that the ideas contained in the Investigation section may provide a useful springboard for any future studies.

A special case is chapter **1** where the project has the potential to use material from throughout the book. As such it could form the basis for how you study the whole module.

The end of each chapter consists of two parts: a check out and consolidation questions. Some of the questions, and their mark allocations, are taken from actual past papers.

Check out

Summarises skills you should now be able to demonstrate having completed this chapter.

At the end of the book you will find two realistic practice papers and their corresponding data sheets.

Answers for all questions are provided.

Graphs and networks

1

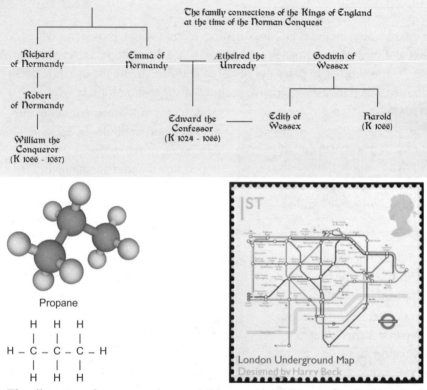

The family connections of the Kings of England at the time of the Norman Conquest

Richard of Normandy

Emma of Normandy

Æthelred the Unready

Godwin of Wessex

Robert of Normandy

Edward the Confessor (K 1024 - 1066)

Edith of Wessex

Harold (K 1066)

William the Conqueror (K 1066 - 1087)

Propane

```
    H   H   H
    |   |   |
H – C – C – C – H
    |   |   |
    H   H   H
```

|ST

London Underground Map
Designed by Harry Beck

The diagrams above are relevant to history, chemistry and transport planning. While the family tree illustrates competing claims to the English throne which would decisively change the course of history, the transport map has a much more immediate importance if you need to cross London. However, the common feature of all three examples is that what is being represented is the 'connectedness' of a system. For example, by stripping away other complexities and reducing a situation to the essential details of connectedness, the mathematician Arthur Cayley was able to successfully analyse molecular structures.

▶ A graph provides the simplest possible way of representing and understanding connectedness in many different situations

You will find that an excellent feature of the subject of this textbook is that it depends on very little prior mathematical knowledge! However, there will be quite a few definitions of new terms with which you will need to become familiar.

> ▶ A **simple graph** is a set of points, called **vertices**, where each pair of distinct vertices may be joined by at most a single line, called an **edge**

The simple graph for a molecule of propane gas is therefore just

> ▶ The degree of a vertex is the number of edges meeting at that vertex

The simple graph of the propane molecule therefore has eight vertices of degree one (representing Hydrogen atoms) and three vertices of degree four (representing Carbon atoms).

Preparation

Before you start this chapter, you should be able to
- **Draw simple graphs and recognise their important features**
1 For a simple graph with three vertices
   a) How many different graphs are there?
   b) Draw each simple graph and list the numbers of vertices of each degree.

Challenge

'In any group of six people at a party, there must be either three people who all know each other, or three people, no two of whom know each other.'

Reword this statement as a statement about simple graphs.
Is this statement always true?

1.1 The language of graphs

This simple graph represents three driving routes between Manchester and London.

For the purpose of choosing between these three routes, it is clear that more information is needed.

Many applications of graphs require more information *about* connections than just whether or not there is a connection. For the example above, you might need

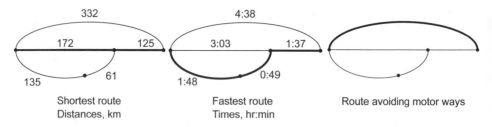

Shortest route
Distances, km

Fastest route
Times, hr:min

Route avoiding motor ways

The routes shown on each diagram are the shortest route, the fastest route and the recommended route if motorways are to be avoided.

It is conventional to call a graph which has numerical values on its edges a **network**. However, you do not need to worry about this distinction since in many applications the words 'graph' and 'network' are used interchangeably.

▶ The general term for the number on an edge is **weight** or **edge weight**

Some of the largest graphs that have been scientifically studied come from telephone billing records. These graphs have millions of vertices (telephone numbers) and millions of edges (calls from one number to another). These graphs illustrate many of the important words used to describe graphs and networks.

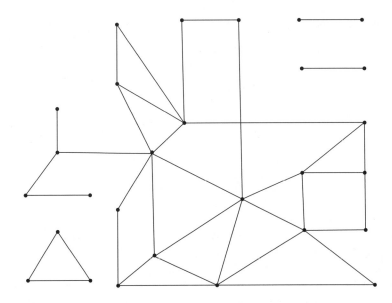

Typically, telephone call graphs tend to have one huge, interconnected component but also many pairs of telephones that only call each other.

> ▶ A graph is called **disconnected** if there is at least one pair of vertices which cannot be connected by a route

> ▶ A graph is called **connected** if all pairs of vertices can be connected by a route

A graph is either connected or disconnected.

Researchers must choose whether to represent a call from A to B by a **directed** edge or by an **undirected** edge.

> ▶ In a directed edge, an arrow is used to indicate the direction of the edge
>
> A ———▶——— B

Which is best depends upon the purpose of the study. In terms of who pays the bill, a directed edge must be used!

Some applications of graphs involve

multiple edges   two or more edges joining the same pair of vertices

and   **loops**   edges joining a vertex to itself.

If a loop connects a vertex to itself, then it contributes two the degree of the vertex.

▶ If a graph contains multiple edges, loops or directed edges, then it is not a simple graph

The following five chapters of this book are concerned with the solution of particular problems on networks. The methods of solution will be given as sequences of procedures which can be followed by rote. These procedures can easily be translated into code to enable a computer to tackle a real-world problem or can be applied, by hand, to solve small-scale problems.

▶ A sequence of procedures to be followed is called an **algorithm**

The word **algorithm** is derived from the Latin name of the Persian mathematician, al-Khwarizmi. The procedures or algorithms that he was interested in were those for solving equations and you will have used his procedures many times. Consider, for example, the following solution.

$$4x - 7 = 3x \qquad \text{Make all quantities positive}$$
$$4x = 3x + 7 \qquad \text{Collect like terms together}$$
$$x = 7$$

Al-Khwarizmi called the first of these procedures, in which all quantities are made positive, 'restoration' or 'al-jabra'. Our word algebra is derived from this word. However, al-Khwarizmi himself did not use any algebraic symbols, but wrote everything out in words!

Exercise 1.1

1 The diagram is a map of some of the
roads in an estate.
   a) Represent this road system
   with a graph, using a vertex
   to represent a road junction
   and an edge to represent
   a road joining two junctions.
   b) Is your graph a simple graph?

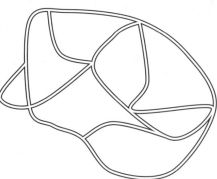

2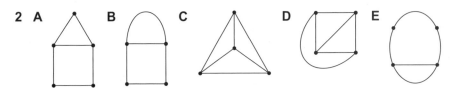

   Look at the graphs shown and state
   a) which are simple graphs
   b) which pairs of graphs are the same.

3 The following algorithm can be applied to any graph.

   | **1** Add up the degrees of all the vertices |
   | **2** Divide the total by 2 |

   a) Apply this algorithm to the graph of a propane molecule.
   b) What does the algorithm find?
   c) Is your result for part **b)** true in general?

p.4

4 If possible, draw graphs with precisely:
   a) 3 vertices of degree 1 and 3 vertices of degree 3
   b) 2 vertices of degree 1 and 3 vertices of degree 3
   c) 1 vertex of degree 1 and 3 vertices of degree 3

1.2 Cycles, paths and trails

> ▶ A **path** through a graph is a route connecting two vertices such that no vertex is passed through more than once

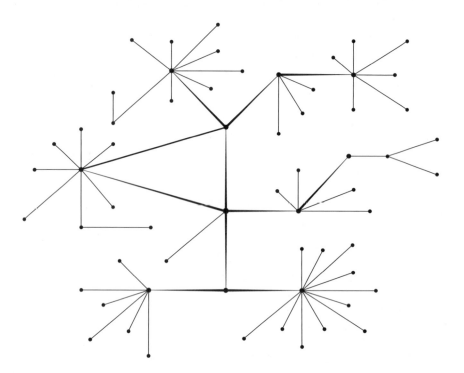

The World Wide Web is a connected graph containing some 8 billion documents. A random search for a particular document would not be practical and so considerable effort is put into developing efficient methods of searching using paths that are relatively short. It is estimated that an 'intelligent agent' can navigate between any two documents using a path with no more than 19 links.

> ▶ A **cycle** is a path where the initial and final vertices are the same

A typical day's telephone call graph for the author, the author's wife, sister-in-law and mother-in-law contains a cycle of length three.

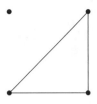

Since a cycle is a special kind of path, no vertex can be passed through twice.

Example 1

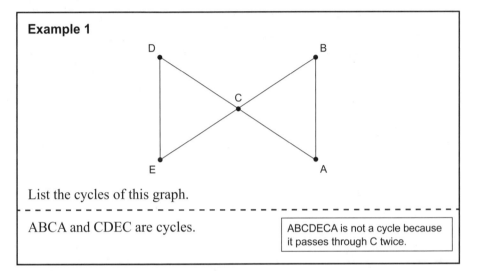

List the cycles of this graph.

- -

ABCA and CDEC are cycles.

> ABCDECA is not a cycle because it passes through C twice.

For some applications, you may need to find routes which pass through a vertex more than once.

> ► A **trail** is a route connecting two vertices which can pass through vertices more than once but does not pass along the same edge more than once

In Example **1**, BCDECA is a trail.

However, BCDECB is not a trail because edge BC is used twice.

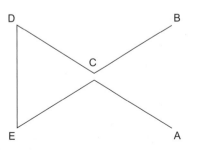

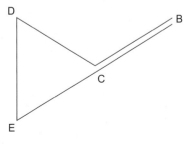

1.3 Matrices

The algorithms that are used to solve real world problems on large networks have to be carried out by computers. All the information on such a network must therefore be stored in numerical form.

It is straightforward to put this information into the form of a rectangular table of numbers. The number 1 shows that a pair of vertices is connected by an edge and the number 0 shows that they are not connected.

	A	B	C	D
A	0	1	0	1
B	1	0	1	1
C	0	1	0	1
D	1	1	1	0

▶ Any rectangular array of numbers is called a **matrix**

The matrix shown above is called an **adjacency matrix** because it shows which pairs of vertices are adjacent to each other, that is, directly connected by an edge. It represents this graph.

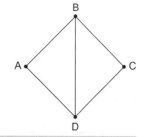

▶ The diagonal from the top left to the bottom right of a square matrix is called the **main diagonal**

The graph shown above has no loops and so the elements on the main diagonal are all zero. The graph has no directed edges and so the matrix is symmetrical about its main diagonal.

An example of a directed graph and its associated matrix is

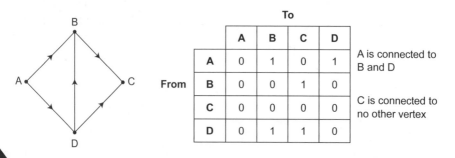

		To			
		A	B	C	D
From	A	0	1	0	1
	B	0	0	1	0
	C	0	0	0	0
	D	0	1	1	0

A is connected to B and D

C is connected to no other vertex

More generally, a **matrix of edge weights** uses the weight on an edge in place of the number 1 that was used earlier in the adjacency matrix. For example, the network of road distances between Manchester and London would be represented as shown.

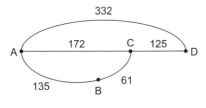

	A	B	C	D
A	0	135	172	332
B	135	0	61	0
C	172	61	0	125
D	332	0	125	0

In practice, you will meet tables of numbers expressed in various forms. For example, road distances are typically given in the triangular form shown below.

	Bordeaux	Calais	Cherbourg	Dijon	Lille	Marseille	Nice	Orléans	Paris	Reims	St. Etienne	Strasbourg
Bordeaux												
Calais	870											
Cherbourg	645	466										
Dijon	646	573	669									
Lille	803	114	504	506								
Marseille	647	1062	1127	502	995							
Nice	804	1219	1284	660	1152	185						
Orléans	458	425	435	302	358	755	912					
Paris	579	290	359	311	223	769	927	132				
Reims	715	275	510	301	208	800	957	268	114			
St. Etienne	516	809	874	250	742	332	490	425	517	547		
Strasbourg	946	621	855	566	530	794	796	614	490	348	542	
Toulouse	244	970	887	724	903	405	563	554	678	815	428	1018

Exercise 1.3

1 Draw a directed graph with adjacency matrix as shown.

$$
\begin{array}{c}
 & & \text{To} \\
 & & \begin{array}{cccc} A & B & C & D \end{array} \\
\text{From} & \begin{array}{c} A \\ B \\ C \\ D \end{array} & \left(\begin{array}{cccc}
0 & 0 & 1 & 1 \\
1 & 0 & 1 & 0 \\
0 & 0 & 0 & 1 \\
0 & 1 & 0 & 0
\end{array}\right)
\end{array}
$$

2 Write down a matrix to represent the graph and a matrix to represent the directed graph shown below.

a)   **b)**

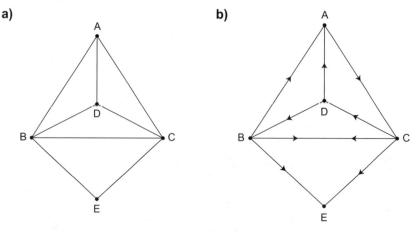

3 Some of the code-words used in the 'even-weight code of length 4' are as shown.

$$0000, \quad 0011, \quad 0110, \quad 1100, \quad 1111$$

a) Draw a network with the five code-words as vertices. Set the weight on an edge between two code-words equal to the number of places in which their binary digits differ.

> The digits 0011 and 0110 differ in two places, their distance is 2.

(This is called the distance between the code-words.)

b) When transmitting and receiving code, what is the advantage in using code-words for which the distances are relatively large?

4 Cape Air is a regional airline. Some of the routes it flies in the Cape Cod area of the United States are shown on the map.

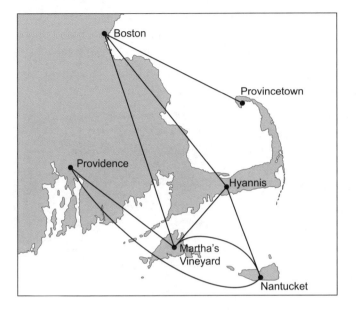

Write down an adjacency matrix for the routes flown by Cape Air. (Put the places in alphabetical order.)

5 Five friends, A, B, C, D and E, keep in touch by sending each other text messages. The costs, in pence, of sending messages between each pair of friends are shown in the table.

	A	B	C	D	E
A	–	16	12	10	17
B	16	–	15	13	12
C	12	15	–	10	14
D	10	13	10	–	11
E	17	12	14	11	–

Draw a network to represent this information.

Investigation – Graphs

In this book you will meet problems involving some of the modern applications of graphs to huge networks, such as those based upon silicon chip technology, the internet and DNA. However, graphs have been important in understanding much smaller systems than these.

The birth of graph theory
In the 18th century, the Prussian city of Konigsberg had seven bridges connecting its two islands to each other and to the North and South banks of the River Pregel.

p.54

The townsfolk realised that, for some reason, it did not seem to be possible to find a route between any two places which would cross each bridge precisely once.

> The seventh bridge is behind the couple.

The Swiss mathematician, Euler, proved rigorously that such a route was indeed impossible. He started his proof by forming an abstract graph where the islands and the North and South banks of the river were represented by vertices. The edges represented direct routes across each of the bridges.

1 Draw an abstract graph to represent the Konigsberg bridges.

> The graph will have multiple edges.

2 What are the degrees of the vertices in your graph?

3 Investigate another system of rivers, islands and bridges of your own choosing.
   a) Does a walking route, which crosses every bridge only once, exist?
   b) Create an abstract graph to represent your system.
   c) List the degrees of the vertices in your graph.

4 Can you see any relationship between the degrees of the vertices in your graphs and whether it is possible to find a suitable walking route?

You will study Euler's proof and its modern applications later in this book.

Leonhard Euler was one of the most prolific and significant mathematicians ever. Born in Basel, Switzerland in 1707 he spent most of his working life in St Petersburg, Russia and Berlin, Prussia.

As well as his work on the Konigsberg bridge problem, he also contributed another famous result on graphs which can be related to the numbers of faces (F), vertices (V) and edges (E) of a convex polyhedron.

$$F + V - E = 2$$

Consolidation

You should now be able to
- Define and use the following terms

Simple graph	Network
Edge	Directed edge
Vertex	Degree of a vertex
Connected graph	Disconnected graph
Cycle	Path
Trail	Algorithm
Adjacency matrix	Matrix of edge weights

On the Use of Mathematics examination papers you will not be tested on the meaning of words such as cycle and trail. However the definitions given in this chapter will be useful when you come across these words in applications of graph theory. Consequently these questions are not typical exam questions.

1 For these graphs, identify which of the following statements are true.

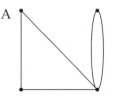
A

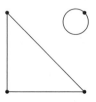
B

C

- **a)** The graph is connected.
- **b)** The graph is simple.
- **c)** The graph contains a vertex of degree 3.
- **d)** The graph contains a vertex of degree 4.
- **e)** The graph contains a loop.
- **f)** The graph contains a cycle.

2 For this graph give three examples each of
- **a)** paths from A to B
- **b)** cycles from A to A

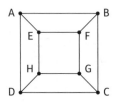

The vertices and edges of this graph correspond to the vertices and edges of a cube.

3 a) Check each of the following statements about this adjacency matrix and explain what each statement implies about the graph that the matrix represents.

$$\begin{array}{c}\begin{array}{cccccc}\text{A} & \text{B} & \text{C} & \text{D} & \text{E} & \text{F}\end{array}\\\begin{array}{c}\text{A}\\\text{B}\\\text{C}\\\text{D}\\\text{E}\\\text{F}\end{array}\left(\begin{array}{cccccc}0 & 0 & 1 & 1 & 0 & 1\\0 & 0 & 0 & 0 & 0 & 0\\1 & 0 & 0 & 1 & 1 & 0\\1 & 0 & 1 & 0 & 1 & 1\\0 & 0 & 1 & 1 & 0 & 0\\1 & 0 & 0 & 1 & 0 & 0\end{array}\right)\end{array}$$

i) The matrix has six rows and columns.

ii) Row B consists only of zeroes.

iii) All the elements are zeroes or ones.

iv) All the elements on the main diagonal are zeroes.

v) The main diagonal is a line of symmetry.

vi) The sum of the elements in row A is three.

vii) The sum of all the elements in the matrix is 14.

b) Draw the graph corresponding to this adjacency matrix.

2 Trees and spanning trees

Deciding the best way to connect all the vertices in a network is an important problem with many applications. A chemical factory may want to connect a set of reactor vessels using the shortest total length of piping, whilst a computer company might want to connect all its machines at the lowest cost.

If a graph has a cycle, then there will be more than one way of moving between some of its vertices. By choosing the 'best' route out of the alternatives such redundancy is removed. This chapter is about such graphs, called trees, and how to find the best one.

▶ A **tree** is a connected graph with no cycles

All the following graphs are trees and one even looks like a tree!

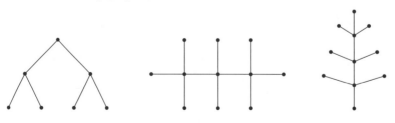

> ▶ Trees are the most widely used of all graphs. Their applications range from internet search programs to mechanical engineering

This network represents the costs of laying cabling between four departments in a college.

Connecting up the departments with these three runs of cabling costs £2260.

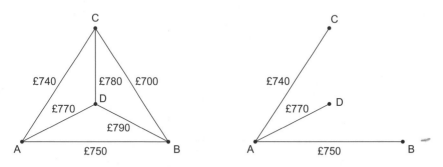

In complicated networks, deciding which is the best possible tree requires practical methods that can be carried out by computers. In this chapter you will learn what is a minimum spanning tree and a greedy algorithm, and how to apply both Prim's and Kruskal's algorithms.

Preparation

Before you start this chapter, you should be able to
- **Investigate small networks 'by hand'**

For the network of four college departments shown above:
1 What is the lowest number of runs of cabling which would connect up the four departments?
2 How many ways are there of connecting up the departments using the lowest number of runs?
3 What is the lowest possible cost of the connection?

Challenge

Research the cost of laying cables between different areas of your college, town or region. Set up a network to represent these costs and try to find the best connections to make.

2.1 Spanning trees

The possible runs of cabling considered in the opening section can be represented by graphs such as the following.

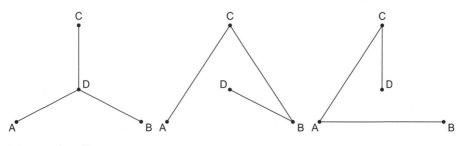

The graphs all

- connect four vertices
- have three edges
- have no cycles

They are therefore trees which 'span' all the vertices.

> ► A **spanning tree** is a tree which connects together all the vertices in a graph
> If the graph has V vertices, then the spanning tree has $V - 1$ edges

The connections given by the spanning trees shown above have costs of £2340, £2230 and £2270, respectively. You want to find the **minimum connector** and what is called the **minimum spanning tree**.

For the four college departments, there are actually 16 possible spanning trees. For such a relatively small number of possibilities, you can easily spot the best connections to use. However, as the number of vertices increases, the number of possible spanning trees increases very rapidly. For just 20 vertices, there are approximately 2.6×10^{23} possible spanning trees. So to find the best method of connection you need an algorithm that can be programmed onto a computer.

The easiest algorithms to understand are those which are called **'greedy'**. This means that you repeatedly make the choice which appears best at that stage without worrying about any long-term consequences of the choice.

For the college departments, you might therefore immediately choose the run of lowest cost.

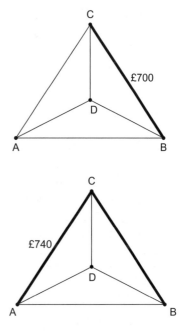

Then you might choose the run with the next lowest cost.

At this point you have to be careful. The next lowest cost is for the run AB. However, there is no point in making this connection since A and B are already connected via C. What would you do next?

As you will see in the next section, the minimum connector problem is actually a very easy problem to solve because this greedy approach *can* be used and it can be proved that it will always produce the best possible solution.

The first algorithm that you will study was published in 1956 by an American mathematician, Joseph Kruskal.

2.2 Kruskal's algorithm

Kruskal's algorithm finds a minimum spanning tree for any connected network. The algorithm selects edges to use by moving down an ordered list of edges and choosing the next edge which does not create a cycle with those already chosen.

If the network has n vertices then the same step will be repeated $n - 1$ times until all vertices are included in the spanning tree.

> **Kruskal's algorithm**
> 1 List all the edges in order of increasing weight
> 2 Choose the edge with lowest weight that does *not* form a cycle with the edges already chosen
>   (If there are several such edges then choose one at random)
> 3 Repeat step **2** until $n - 1$ edges have been chosen

Example 1
Apply Kruskal's algorithm to this network for the college's departments.

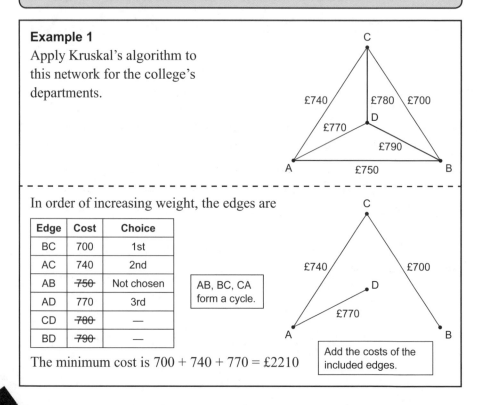

In order of increasing weight, the edges are

Edge	Cost	Choice
BC	700	1st
AC	740	2nd
AB	~~750~~	Not chosen
AD	770	3rd
CD	~~780~~	—
BD	~~790~~	—

AB, BC, CA form a cycle.

Add the costs of the included edges.

The minimum cost is $700 + 740 + 770 = £2210$

Example 2

A cable company has to connect up the villages represented here. The distances are in miles.

a) State the number of edges in a spanning tree.

b) Find a minimum spanning tree for the cable company.

c) State the length of cabling required.

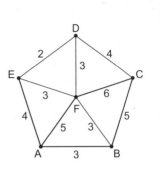

- -

a) 5 edges

b)

Edge	Cost	Choice
DE	2	1st
DF	3	2nd
EF	~~3~~	Not chosen
AB	3	3rd
BF	3	4th
AE	~~4~~	Not chosen
CD	4	5th
AF	~~5~~	—
BC	~~5~~	—
CF	~~6~~	—

At the second iteration there are four edges, DF, EF, AB and BF, all with lowest weight 3. DF is chosen at random.
The minimum spanning tree may not be unique.

At the third iteration EF would form a cycle, with DE and DF, and so is eliminated. Of the remaining two edges with weight 3, AB is chosen at random. Note that at intermediate stages the selected edges do not need to be connected.

c) Cost = 2 + 3 + 3 + 3 + 4 = 15 miles

Exercise 2.2

1 Every Christmas Sam puts lights on nine trees, A, B, C, D, E, F, G, H and I, in his garden. The trees have to be connected together either directly or indirectly by cabling and also connected to the mains electricity supply, M, at the house. The cabling has to be laid alongside the garden paths. The diagram shows the lengths of the paths, in metres.

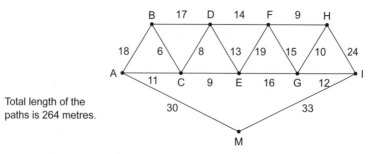

Total length of the paths is 264 metres.

a) Use Kruskal's algorithm to find the minimum length of cabling required. State this minimum length. (*5 marks*)

b) Draw the minimum spanning tree. (*2 marks*)

(AQA 2004)

2 The following network shows the lengths, in miles, of roads connecting seven villages.

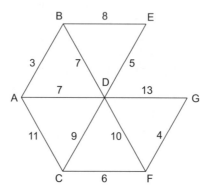

a) Use Kruskal's algorithm to find a minimum spanning tree for the network. (*4 marks*)

b) State the length of your minimum spanning tree. (*1 mark*)

c) There are two minimum spanning trees for this network. Draw both of these minimum spanning trees. (*2 marks*)

(AQA 2005)

3 a) i) State the number of edges in a minimum spanning tree of a network with 10 vertices. *(1 mark)*

ii) State the number of edges in a minimum spanning tree of a network with n vertices. *(1 mark)*

b) The following network has 10 vertices: A, B, …, J. The numbers on each edge represent the distances, in miles, between pairs of vertices.

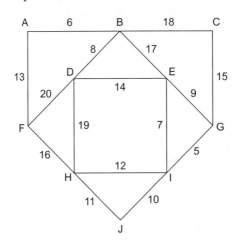

i) Use Kruskal's algorithm to find the minimum spanning tree for the network. *(5 marks)*

ii) State the length of your spanning tree. *(1 mark)*

iii) Draw your spanning tree. *(2 marks)*

2.3 Prim's algorithm

A disadvantage of Kruskal's algorithm is the need to check that you are not creating a cycle whenever you add a new edge. An alternative greedy algorithm was developed by Robert Prim, who worked with Kruskal at Bell Laboratories. This algorithm had been independently developed, much earlier, by a Czech mathematician, Vojtěch Jarník.

Prim's algorithm produces a minimum spanning tree, T, for any connected graph with n vertices. Starting with any arbitrarily chosen vertex, V, in T, the algorithm consists of repeating the same step $n - 1$ times.

Prim's algorithm
1 Start with V in T
2 Add to T the edge of lowest weight between a vertex in T and a vertex not in T
   (If there are several such edges then choose one at random)
3 Repeat step 2 until $n - 1$ edges have been chosen

Example 3
Apply Prim's algorithm to the network of college departments, starting from C.

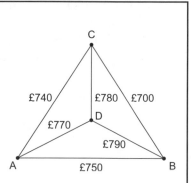

Edge	Vertices of T	Cost
CB	{B, C}	£700
CA	{A, B, C}	£740
AD	{A, B, C, D}	£770

Cost = £2210

Example 4

The following network shows the
lengths, in miles, of roads connecting
nine villages, A, B, …, I.

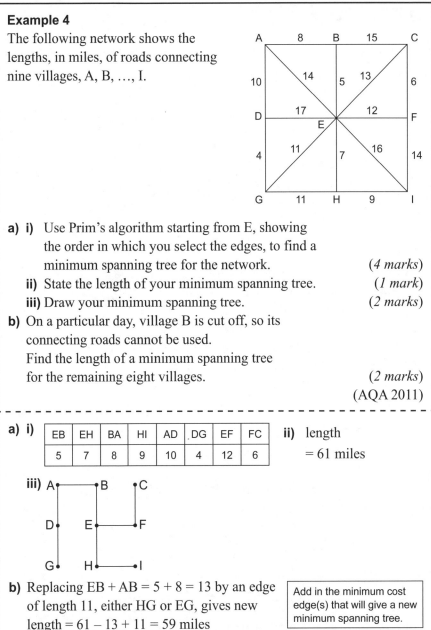

a) i) Use Prim's algorithm starting from E, showing
the order in which you select the edges, to find a
minimum spanning tree for the network. *(4 marks)*

ii) State the length of your minimum spanning tree. *(1 mark)*

iii) Draw your minimum spanning tree. *(2 marks)*

b) On a particular day, village B is cut off, so its
connecting roads cannot be used.
Find the length of a minimum spanning tree
for the remaining eight villages. *(2 marks)*

(AQA 2011)

---

a) i)

EB	EH	BA	HI	AD	DG	EF	FC
5	7	8	9	10	4	12	6

ii) length
= 61 miles

iii)

A•———•B   •C

D•   E•———•F

G•   H•———•I

b) Replacing EB + AB = 5 + 8 = 13 by an edge
of length 11, either HG or EG, gives new
length = 61 − 13 + 11 = 59 miles

> Add in the minimum cost
> edge(s) that will give a new
> minimum spanning tree.

Exercise 2.3

1 The following network shows the lengths, in miles, of roads connecting nine villages.

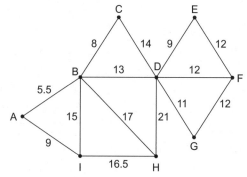

a) Use Prim's algorithm, starting from A, to find a minimum spanning tree for the network. *(5 marks)*

b) Find the length of your minimum spanning tree. *(1 mark)*

c) Draw your minimum spanning tree. *(3 marks)*

d) State the number of other spanning trees that are of the same length as your answer in part **a)**. *(1 mark)*

(AQA 2007)

2 The following network shows the lengths, in miles, of roads connecting 11 villages, A, B, ..., K.

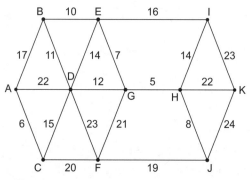

a) Starting from G and showing your working at each stage, use Prim's algorithm to find a minimum spanning for the network. *(6 marks)*

b) State the length of your minimum spanning tree. *(1 mark)*

c) Draw your minimum spanning tree. *(3 marks)*

(AQA 2009)

3 The diagram shows the various ski-runs at a ski resort. There is a shop at S. The manager of the ski resort intends to install a floodlighting system by placing a floodlight at each of the 12 points A, B, . . ., L and at the shop at S. The number on each edge represents the distance, in metres, between two points.

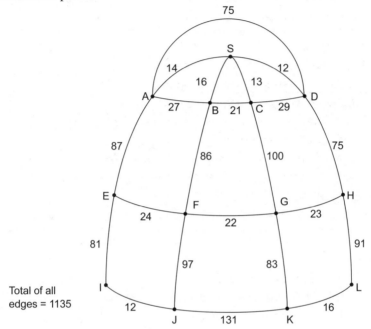

Total of all edges = 1135

The manager wishes to use the minimum amount of cabling, which must be laid along the ski-runs, to connect the 12 points A, B, ..., L and the shop at S.

a) Starting from the shop, and showing your working at each stage, use Prim's algorithm to find the minimum amount of cabling needed to connect the shop and the 12 points. *(5 marks)*

b) State the length of your minimum spanning tree. *(1 mark)*

c) Draw your minimum spanning tree. *(3 marks)*

d) The manager used Kruskal's algorithm to find the minimum spanning tree. Find the seventh and the eighth edges that the manager added to his spanning tree. *(2 marks)*

(AQA 2007)

2.4 Matrix formulation

It is easy to apply Prim's algorithm to a matrix of edge weights. The algorithm can then be programmed so that computers can be used for real world problems.

> **Prim's algorithm**
> 1 Choose a vertex to be the first vertex of T
> 2 Circle the new vertex of T in the top row
> 3 Delete the *row* corresponding to this vertex
> 4 Find the smallest weight remaining in the *columns* corresponding to vertices of T. Circle this weight
> (If there are several such weights then choose one at random)
> 5 The vertex whose *row* contains this weight is then chosen to be the next vertex of T
> 6 Repeat steps **2**, **3**, **4** and **5** until T contains every vertex

---

Example 5

Apply Prim's algorithm, starting from C, to this matrix for the college departments. State the cost of the minimum spanning tree

	A	B	C	D
A	—	750	740	770
B	750	—	700	790
C	740	700	—	780
D	770	790	780	—

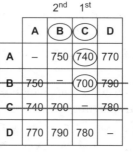

After steps 1, 2, 3, 4

After further steps 5, 2, 3, 4

Completed

CB, CA, AD costs £(740 + 700 + 770) = £2210

Example 6

The lengths of pipelines
between various pumping
stations are as shown.

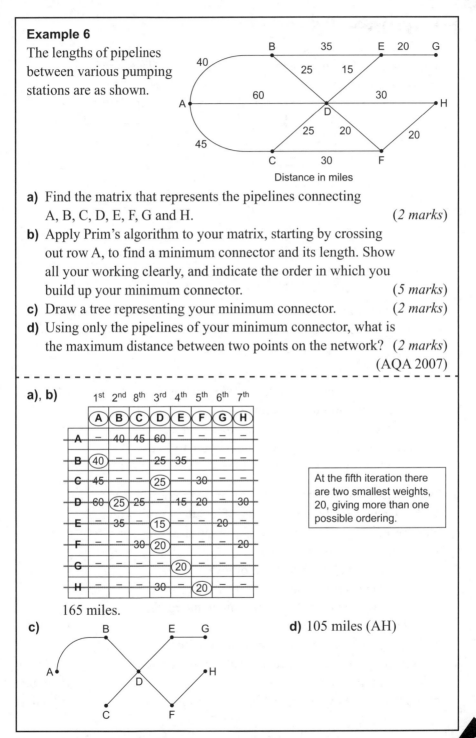

Distance in miles

a) Find the matrix that represents the pipelines connecting
A, B, C, D, E, F, G and H. *(2 marks)*

b) Apply Prim's algorithm to your matrix, starting by crossing
out row A, to find a minimum connector and its length. Show
all your working clearly, and indicate the order in which you
build up your minimum connector. *(5 marks)*

c) Draw a tree representing your minimum connector. *(2 marks)*

d) Using only the pipelines of your minimum connector, what is
the maximum distance between two points on the network? *(2 marks)*

(AQA 2007)

---

a), b)

1st 2nd 8th 3rd 4th 5th 6th 7th

	A	B	C	D	E	F	G	H
A	–	40	45	60	–	–	–	–
B	(40)	–	–	25	35	–	–	–
C	45	–	–	(25)	–	30	–	–
D	60	(25)	25	–	15	20	–	30
E	–	35	–	(15)	–	–	20	–
F	–	–	30	(20)	–	–	–	20
G	–	–	–	–	(20)	–	–	–
H	–	–	–	30	–	(20)	–	–

At the fifth iteration there
are two smallest weights,
20, giving more than one
possible ordering.

165 miles.

c)

d) 105 miles (AH)

33

Exercise 2.4

1 The road distances in kilometres between eight villages are shown in this table.

	A	B	C	D	E	F	G	H
A	—	9	8	6	6	5	3	6
B	9	—	7	10	5	7	8	7
C	8	7	—	5	4	3	8	9
D	6	10	5	—	5	3	8	10
E	6	5	4	5	—	2	4	5
F	5	7	3	3	2	—	5	6
G	3	8	8	8	4	5	—	3
H	6	7	9	10	5	6	3	—

There is a shortage of water and a desalination plant is to be built at A, near the sea. The local authority intends to lay a new system of water-pipes alongside some of the roads.

a) Use Prim's algorithm, starting from A, to find a minimum spanning tree for the eight villages. *(4 marks)*

b) Draw your minimum spanning tree. *(2 marks)*

c) State the minimum length of piping required. *(1 mark)*

d) Give **two** reasons why your solution to part **a)** may not be the solution adopted by the local authority. *(2 marks)*

2 Two towns, A and B, are 30 miles apart by motorway. The towns are both connected by minor roads, of lengths 15 miles and 25 miles respectively, to town C. The average speed for journeys can be assumed to be 40 mph on the minor roads and 60 mph on the motorway.

a) Write down a minimum connector for distances. How long would it take to drive along the roads of this minimum connector? *(3 marks)*

b) Write down a minimum connector for times. How long would it take to drive along the roads of this minimum connector? *(3 marks)*

c) Why are the times of **a)** and **b)** not the same? *(1 mark)*

3 Six of the main tourist attractions in a city are denoted by A, B, C, D, E and F. The numbers shown in the table represent the road distances between these attractions, in kilometres.

	A	B	C	D	E	F
A	—	3	5	4	7	8
B	3	—	6	1	6	9
C	5	6	—	4	5	8
D	4	1	4	—	2	7
E	7	6	5	2	—	5
F	8	9	8	7	5	—

The city council is to connect these attractions with a computer system. The cabling for this system is to be laid alongside some of the existing roads.

a) i) Use Prim's algorithm, starting from A, to find a minimum spanning for the six attractions. Indicate the order in which you select the edges. *(5 marks)*
　ii) State the minimum length of cabling needed. *(1 mark)*
　iii) Draw your minimum spanning tree. *(2 marks)*
b) Give a reason why your solution to part **a)** may not be the solution chosen by the city council. *(1 mark)*
c) i) There is already a suitable cable connecting D and F. In addition to this cable, find the minimum length of cabling required to connect the six attractions. *(2 marks)*
　ii) The council finds that it cannot lay a cable connecting CD directly. Find the extra amount of cabling that is now required to complete the minimum spanning tree. *(2 marks)*

Investigation – Spanning trees

Gustav Kirchhoff was a German theoretical physicist born in Konigsberg in 1824. He formulated laws describing light spectra and the laws governing the currents and voltage drops in electrical circuits.

His two circuit laws are now central to the study of electrical engineering and rely heavily upon various graph-theoretic ideas.

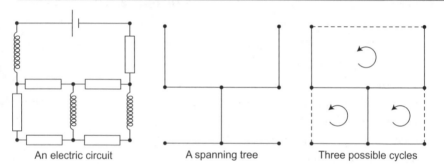

An electric circuit   A spanning tree   Three possible cycles

Starting with a spanning tree, whenever Kirchhoff added back a deleted edge this created a cycle. He proved that applying his laws to precisely these cycles always allowed him to find a solution to the full equations.

1   How many edges E and vertices V does the electric circuit have?

2   a) How many edges does the spanning tree have?
    b) How many cycles can be formed by adding back in a deleted edge?

3   a) Repeat questions **1** and **2** for an electric circuit of your own choosing.
    b) Can you obtain a general formula for the number of cycles formed?

Research
Find out more about Kirchhoff's contributions to electrical engineering and Kirchhoff's Laws. Investigate the connection between the formula of question **3b)** and a result known as Euler's formula for planar graphs.

The most important modern applications of trees are in searches of data and decision making in business. To get an appreciation of the clarity that trees can bring to a problem, consider this logic puzzle.

> You have nine coins, one of which is too light – it is a counterfeit. You have a balance which can be used to compare the weights of any two sets of coins. What is the minimum number of weighings that you need to identify the counterfeit coin?

Each vertex of the tree represents a weighing with three possible outcomes.

If the initial weighing gives weight $\{1, 2, 3\}$ < weight $\{7, 8, 9\}$ then take the left-hand branch and weigh coin 1 against coin 3.

If the initial weighing gives weight $\{1, 2, 3\}$ = weight $\{7, 8, 9\}$ then take the middle branch and weigh coin 4 against coin 6.

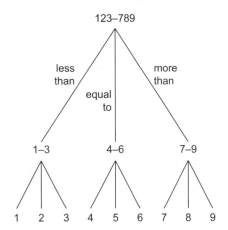

In this way the bottom line identifies the counterfeit coin in two weighings.

4 You are given four coins one of which is counterfeit – it may be too heavy or too light. Draw a tree diagram to show how you would determine the counterfeit coin in the minimum number of weighings.

> You can assume that you have other coins which you know are genuine.

Project

Devise your own algorithm to obtain a minimum spanning tree by *deleting* edges.
You will need to decide when an edge *cannot* be deleted.

Consolidation

Check out

You should now be able to
► Find minimal spanning trees by applying
  Kruskal's algorithm
  Prim's algorithm, including the matrix formulation

1 The network shows 10 towns. The times, in minutes, to travel between
  pairs of towns are indicated on the edges.

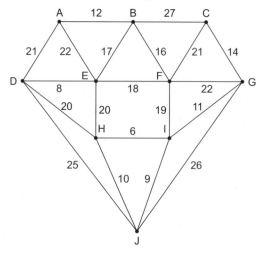

a) Use Kruskal's algorithm, showing the order
   in which you select the edges, to find a
   minimum spanning tree for the 10 towns. *(6 marks)*
b) State the length of your minimum spanning tree. *(1 mark)*
c) Draw your minimum spanning tree. *(3 marks)*
d) If Prim's algorithm, starting at B, had been used to
   find the minimum spanning tree, state which edge
   would have been the final edge to complete the
   minimum spanning tree. *(1 mark)*

(AQA 2010)

2 A group of 8 friends, A, B, C, D, E, F, G and H, keep in touch by sending text messages. The cost, in pence, of sending a message between each pair of friends is shown in the table.

	A	B	C	D	E	F	G	H
A	—	15	10	12	16	11	14	17
B	15	—	15	14	15	16	16	15
C	10	15	—	11	10	12	14	9
D	12	14	11	—	11	12	14	12
E	16	15	10	11	—	13	15	14
F	11	16	12	12	13	—	14	8
G	14	16	14	14	15	14	—	13
H	17	15	9	12	14	8	13	—

One of the group wishes to pass on a piece of news to all the other friends, either by a direct text or by the message being passed on from friend to friend, at the minimum total cost.

a) Use Prim's algorithm, starting from A, showing the order in which you select the edges, to find a minimum spanning tree for the table. *(4 marks)*

  i) Draw your minimum spanning tree. *(2 marks)*

  ii) Find the minimum total cost. *(1 mark)*

b) Person H leaves the group. Find the new minimum total cost. *(2 marks)*

(AQA 2011)

3 The following network shows the roads connecting seven villages, A, B, C, ... G. The number on each edge represents the length, in miles, between a pair of villages.

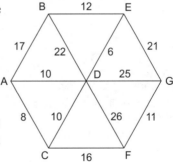

a) Use Prim's algorithm, starting from D, to find the length of a minimum spanning tree for this network. *(6 marks)*

b) There are two minimum spanning trees for this network. Draw both of these minimum spanning trees. *(3 marks)*

(AQA 2012)

3 Shortest paths

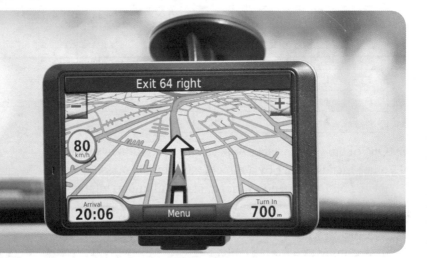

The classic example of a **shortest path problem** is to find the 'shortest' route between two fixed points on a map. Represented as a network the edges may represent the available roads or railways or air routes, etc. whilst the edge weights can be the associated distances or travel times or costs, etc. Knowing how to find the shortest, fastest or least expensive route can clearly give a company a commercial advantage.

▶ Finding the 'best' route is crucially important in moving goods and people in and between cities. It is equally important in moving data at high speeds through networks such as the internet

Not all shortest path problems involve a physical network. Six degrees of Separation is the idea that any two people on Earth are connected by a chain of no more than five acquaintances, that is, six friendships.

You — ? — ? — ? — ? — ? — President of America

The smallness of these degrees of separation can have important social consequences. In an interconnected world, the shorter the connections, the faster cultural and scientific ideas can spread, increasing their impact. Unfortunately false rumours and viruses (biological and electronic) can also spread rapidly and be harder to contain.

A light hearted variant of this idea is provided by this game for film buffs who have to try to connect a given film actor/actress to Kevin Bacon using as few intermediaries as possible. A simple network is shown below.

An edge indicates that the actors appeared in a film together. Kevin Bacon and John Cleese both appeared in *The Big Picture*. Cameron Diaz has not been in a film with Kevin Bacon but did appear in *Shrek Forever After* with John Cleese. This gives John Cleese a distance 1 and Cameron Diaz a distance 2 from Kevin Bacon.

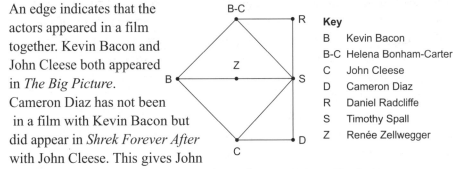

Key
B   Kevin Bacon
B-C Helena Bonham-Carter
C   John Cleese
D   Cameron Diaz
R   Daniel Radcliffe
S   Timothy Spall
Z   Renée Zellwegger

Dijkstra's algorithm

For many of the examples you will meet in this chapter you may be able to spot the shortest path immediately. In practice, applications can involve billions of connections and so a fast algorithm is needed which can be programmed into a computer.

The idea is to work outwards through the network from a starting vertex calculating the lengths of the paths to neighbouring vertices using the edges investigated so far and assigning **temporary labels** to record the shortest distances found so far. As soon as you are sure that a shortest path to a vertex has been found you give it a **permanent label**. You then start from this vertex and (re)calculate the temporary labels for its neighbours using its permanent label as a starting distance. You stop when you assign a permanent label to your destination vertex.

> If you know a shortest path from X to Y via Z then this path must use a shortest path from X to Z.

Example 1

Find the shortest path from A to D.

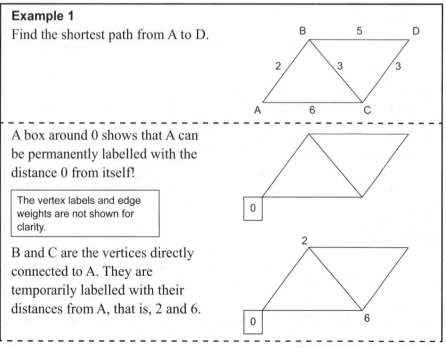

A box around 0 shows that A can be permanently labelled with the distance 0 from itself!

> The vertex labels and edge weights are not shown for clarity.

B and C are the vertices directly connected to A. They are temporarily labelled with their distances from A, that is, 2 and 6.

▶ Continued on next page

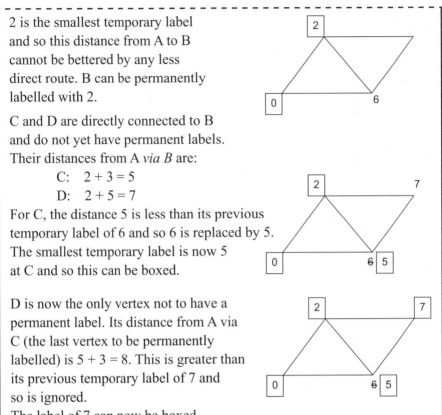

2 is the smallest temporary label and so this distance from A to B cannot be bettered by any less direct route. B can be permanently labelled with 2.

C and D are directly connected to B and do not yet have permanent labels. Their distances from A *via B* are:

C: $2 + 3 = 5$
D: $2 + 5 = 7$

For C, the distance 5 is less than its previous temporary label of 6 and so 6 is replaced by 5. The smallest temporary label is now 5 at C and so this can be boxed.

D is now the only vertex not to have a permanent label. Its distance from A via C (the last vertex to be permanently labelled) is $5 + 3 = 8$. This is greater than its previous temporary label of 7 and so is ignored.
The label of 7 can now be boxed.

The procedure used in example **1** was developed by and named after the Dutch computer scientist, Edsger Dijkstra.

Dijkstra's algorithm

1 Label the initial vertex with permanent label 0

2 If V is the vertex you have just permanently labelled, update those vertices that are directly connected to it and do not have a permanent label. For each such vertex X
- Calculate, value of label at V + weight of VX
- Make this the temporary label if it is smaller than its current label

3 Make the vertex with the smallest temporary label permanent. (If there is more than one smallest temporary label then chose one at random)

4 Stop if the final vertex has a permanent label. Otherwise, go to step **2**

Example 2

The network shows the pathways connecting different departments at a college. The number on each edge represents the time taken, in minutes, to walk along that pathway.

a) i) Use Dijkstra's algorithm on the network to find the minimum walking time from T to E.

ii) Write down the corresponding route.

b) State the minimum walking time from T to M.

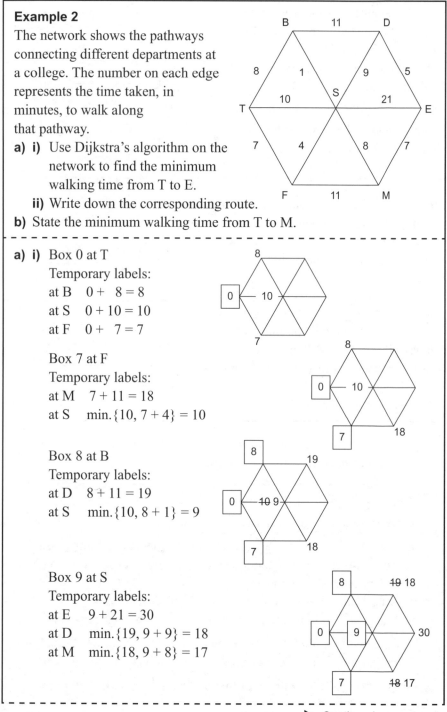

a) i) Box 0 at T

Temporary labels:

at B $0 + 8 = 8$

at S $0 + 10 = 10$

at F $0 + 7 = 7$

Box 7 at F

Temporary labels:

at M $7 + 11 = 18$

at S   min. $\{10, 7 + 4\} = 10$

Box 8 at B

Temporary labels:

at D $8 + 11 = 19$

at S   min. $\{10, 8 + 1\} = 9$

Box 9 at S

Temporary labels:

at E $9 + 21 = 30$

at D   min. $\{19, 9 + 9\} = 18$

at M   min. $\{18, 9 + 8\} = 17$

► Continued on next page

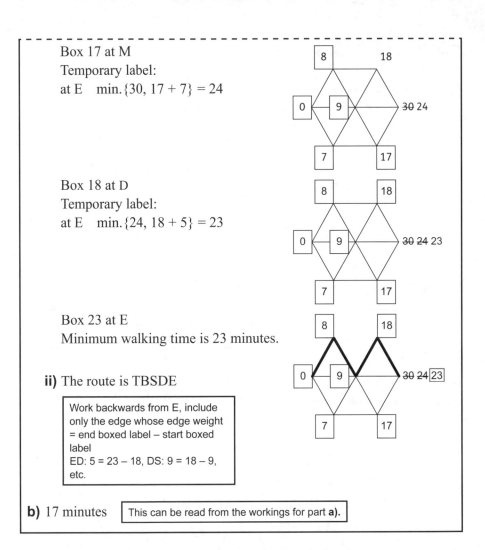

Box 17 at M
Temporary label:
at E   min. $\{30, 17 + 7\} = 24$

Box 18 at D
Temporary label:
at E   min. $\{24, 18 + 5\} = 23$

Box 23 at E
Minimum walking time is 23 minutes.

ii) The route is TBSDE

> Work backwards from E, include
> only the edge whose edge weight
> = end boxed label – start boxed
> label
> ED: 5 = 23 – 18, DS: 9 = 18 – 9,
> etc.

b) 17 minutes | This can be read from the workings for part **a).**

▶ Once Dijkstra's algorithm has been carried out you know the shortest
paths to *all* permanently labelled vertices; not just the final vertex

When writing out your solution to a problem such as Example **2**, you should
show all your working. So, at S, you must show ~~10~~ as well as $\boxed{9}$.

Similarly, at E, you must show ~~30 24~~ $\boxed{23}$.

▶ To show that you have used Dijkstra's algorithm to solve a problem
you must show both temporary and permanent labels on a vertex

Exercise 3.1

1 The diagram shows a network of roads. The weight on each edge represents the number of traffic lights along that stretch of road.

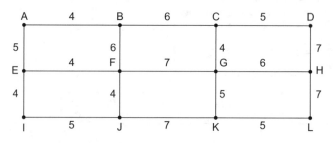

a) Using Dijkstra's algorithm, show that there are two possible routes from A to L with the minimal number of traffic lights. *(6 marks)*

b) Find a route from A to L with the minimum number of traffic lights if the road from A to B is closed. *(2 marks)*

2 The network shows some paths on an estate. The number on each edge represents the time Pete takes, in minutes, to walk along that path.

a) i) Use Dijkstra's algorithm to find the minimum walking time from A to L. *(6 marks)*

   ii) Write down the corresponding route. *(1 mark)*

b) Pete walks from A to L calling at the shop at J. Obtain his fastest route now, giving its time and explaining your method. *(2 marks)*

3 It is required to find the shortest paths from each of A, B and C to K. The number on each edge of the network shows the length of the path in kilometres.

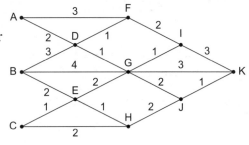

a) How can all three of these paths be determined by applying Dijkstra's algorithm just once? *(1 mark)*

b) Obtain the three shortest paths. Which of A, B and C is nearest to K? *(7 marks)*

4 The number on each edge of this network represents the time, in minutes, taken to walk along a path.

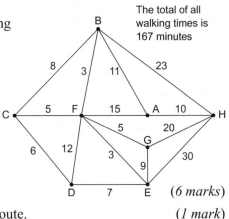

a) i) Use Dijkstra's algorithm to find the minimum walking time from A to J. *(6 marks)*

ii) Write down the corresponding route. *(1 mark)*

b) What is the minimum walking time from A to J via E? *(3 marks)*

5 The diagram shows roads connecting some places of interest in Berlin. The numbers represent the times taken, in minutes, to walk along the roads.

Mia is staying at D and is to visit H.

The total of all walking times is 167 minutes

a) Use Dijkstra's algorithm to find the minimum time to walk from D to H. *(6 marks)*

b) Write down the corresponding route. *(1 mark)*

(AQA 2009)

Investigation – **Shortest paths**

The question of whether computers can think is like the question of whether submarines can swim.

Edsger Wybe Dijkstra (1930–2002)

1 Explain in your own words what Dijkstra probably meant by the quotation above. Do you think he was correct?

Edsger Dijkstra was a computer scientist who, in 1957, published a paper only three pages long, describing two algorithms.

- A variant of Kruskal's algorithm for finding minimum spanning trees.
- The algorithm for finding shortest paths which is now named after him.

In the 1950s, interest in shortest path problems centred upon telephone routing, military logistics and transportation of manufactured goods and food products.

Research

Investigate the work on algorithms carried out during the 1950s.

2 How many different algorithms for solving shortest path problems can you find?

Many shortest path problems involve negative weights on edges. For example, there may be a profit (or negative cost) for a haulage firm in using a particular route.

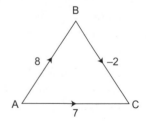

3 What goes wrong if you apply Dijkstra's algorithm to the graph above?

▶ Dijkstra's algorithm *cannot* be used for graphs with negative weights and so other algorithms have been developed for such applications

A graph can be used to represent the prices and exchange rates of commodities and currencies. The diagram represents an instance when a gram of gold was priced at $53.08 or £33.43. The exchange rate was $1 = £0.63.

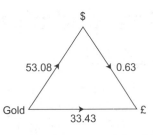

4 For the example above, what price would you receive for a gram of gold if you sold it for dollars and then converted these into pounds?

> **ICT opportunity**
>
> Find up-to-date exchange rates for various currencies. Use a spread sheet to store these rates and to calculate the rates when pairs of transactions are combined.

The solution to question **4** shows that your preferred option should be to sell for dollars and then convert. In practice, such opportunities for *arbitrage* (the exploitation of buying and selling options on different markets) occur all the time. Computers are programmed to automatically exercise such trades as the opportunities arise. However, such trading can be risky because the activities of the competing traders rapidly affect the differences in prices which are very small and constantly changing. The arbitrageur with the fastest computer and the best algorithm has the advantage.

5 a) In what way does problem **4** resemble a shortest path problem?
   b) How does it differ from a shortest path problem?

> **Project**
>
> Throughout the country there are proposals for new motorways, by-passes, tram lines and rail links. For such a scheme:
>
> **1** Create a network diagram showing at least five possible routes.
> **2** Investigate the costs associated with various stages of each route.
> **3** Find the 'best' route.
> **4** Is your solution likely to be the one used?
> **5** How could you make your analysis more realistic?

Consolidation

1 The network represents the footpaths connecting 12 buildings on a university campus. The number on each edge represents the time taken, in minutes, to walk along a footpath.

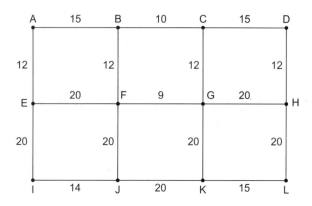

a) i) Use Dijkstra's algorithm to find the minimum time to walk from A to L. (*7 marks*)

   ii) State the corresponding route. (*1 mark*)

b) A new footpath is to be constructed. There are two possibilities:

   from A to D, with a walking time of 30 minutes;

   or from A to I, with a walking time of 20 minutes.

   Determine which of the two alternative new footpaths would reduce the walking time from A to L by the greater amount. (*3 marks*)

(AQA 2007)

2 The diagram shows a network of roads connecting 8 places near Manchester. The number on each edge is the length, in miles, of the road.

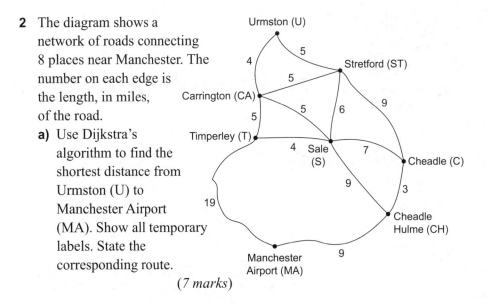

a) Use Dijkstra's algorithm to find the shortest distance from Urmston (U) to Manchester Airport (MA). Show all temporary labels. State the corresponding route.

(7 marks)

b) On a particular day, the road from Stretford (ST) to Cheadle (C) was closed. Find the minimum distance form Urmston (U) to Manchester Airport (MA) on that day. *(3 marks)*

(AQA 2009)

3 The network shows the lengths of roads, in miles, connecting 10 towns, A, B, …, J.

a) Use Dijkstra's algorithm on the network to find the shortest distance from A to J. Show all your working at each vertex. *(7 marks)*

b) Write down the corresponding route. *(1 mark)*

c) A new road is to be constructed connecting B to G. Find the length of this new road if the shortest distance from A to J is reduced by 10 miles. State the new route. *(3 marks)*

(AQA 2012)

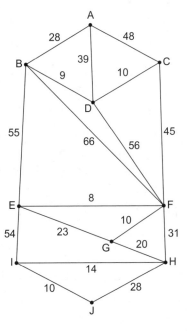

Route inspection

East Lancashire snow: Storm over gritting

Only a third of highways are being treated, leaving side roads and cul-de-sacs in a horrific state.   Lancashire Telegraph, 22.12.09

Lancashire County Council typically spends £4 million each year on its winter service and spreads over 20 000 tonnes of salt on its highways. It is responsible for approximately 7000 km of highways, of which some 2400 km have a priority for gritting.

Ideally you would want a road gritter to follow a circular route that includes every road to be gritted only once and as few other roads as possible. The UK Audit Commission measures the efficiency of a route by the fraction

Distance of highway salted ÷ Total distance travelled

The Commission found that across 31 county divisions this efficiency ranged from 56% to 80% and concluded that better routing could raise all these results to 70% or better. This represents a potentially considerable saving in time, money and lives.

Similar problems arise in other fields. Oil companies may want to use a Pipeline Inspection Gauge, or pig, to efficiently clean and test the structural integrity of a set of pipes in a network, whilst an internet company may want to check that none of the web links between a collection of pages are broken. All of these problems fall into the general class of route inspection problems.

> ▶ The basic idea of route inspection is to find the shortest possible length of a continuous route which uses every edge of a graph at least once and whose initial and final vertices are the same

Preparation

Before you start this chapter, you should be able to

- **Use standard terminology**

1 Define the terms trail and degree of a vertex.

- **Investigate small networks by hand**

2 **a)** How many vertices of this graph have odd degree?

   b) Find a continuous route which uses every edge of this graph at least once and whose initial and final vertices are the same. How many edges did you need to use more than once?

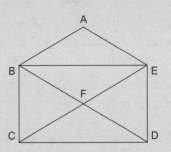

Challenge

Research an example in your own area for an activity such as spraying roads with salt-grit, routing garbage collection, scheduling police patrols or street-sweeping.

Set up a network for the edges being covered and try to find the best possible route for the activity.

4.1 Eulerian trails

> An **Eulerian trail** is a trail which contains every edge in a graph once

Euler demonstrated that this graph representing the bridges of Konigsberg could *not* have an Eulerian trail.

His reasoning was as follows.

Suppose that there was an Eulerian trail from, say, vertex A to vertex B.

Whenever a vertex X not equal to A or B occurs in this trail, it is adjacent to two successive edges: 'in' and 'out'. Since every occurrence of X must involve a pair of edges and no edge is repeated the degree of vertex X must be even.

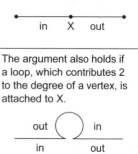

The argument also holds if a loop, which contributes 2 to the degree of a vertex, is attached to X.

However, the graph of the bridges has four vertices of odd degree and so cannot have an Eulerian trail.

Euler's reasoning gives the following general results about graphs with Eulerian trails.

> If a graph G has an Eulerian trail which starts and finishes at the same vertex, then every vertex of G has even degree
> If a graph G has an Eulerian trail which starts and finishes at different vertices, then the end vertices have odd degree and every other vertex of G has even degree

As a consequence, for an Eulerian trail to exist a graph must have no vertices of odd degree (all vertices have even degree) or exactly two vertices of odd degree.

Nearly 100 years after Euler's death, the converse of Euler's result was proved to be true. That is, if every vertex of a connected graph has even degree, then the graph *must* have an Eulerian trail which starts and finishes at the same vertex.

Example 1

Find the number of vertices of this graph which have odd degree. Hence state whether or not this graph has an Eulerian trail.

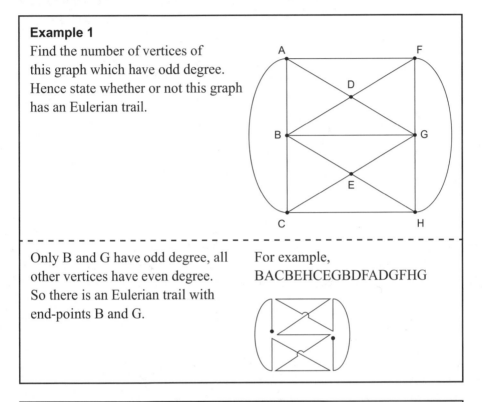

Only B and G have odd degree, all other vertices have even degree. So there is an Eulerian trail with end-points B and G.

For example,
BACBEHCEGBDFADGFHG

Example 2

Explain whether or not it is possible to draw this picture without taking your pencil off the paper and without going over any part of your drawing again.

If this were possible, then this graph would have an Eulerian trail. Since the graph has four odd vertices this is *not* possible.

Exercise 4.1

1 For each of the following graphs, find the number of vertices that have odd degree. Hence state whether or not the graph has an Eulerian trail.

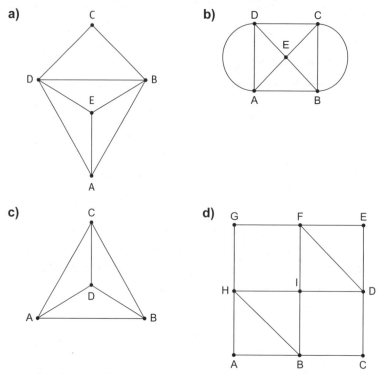

a)

b)

c)

d)

2 Explain why the number of odd vertices in any graph is always an even number.

3 An exhibition is to be held in the series of interconnecting rooms shown here. Is it possible to design a route so that a visitor can enter at A and leave at B, having been through every doorway precisely once? Explain your answer.

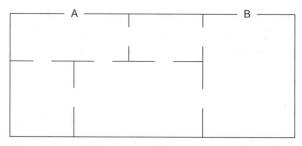

4 Explain whether or not it is possible to draw this picture without taking your pencil off the paper and without going over any part of your drawing again.

If possible, describe a route.

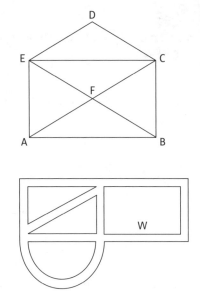

5 Vicki lives at Willow Farm, W, and delivers a village newsletter to her neighbours. The roads are as illustrated. Can she deliver the magazine without having to walk along any road twice?

6 a) Four villages are joined by 6 footpaths as shown. Explain why it is not possible to find a closed trail containing each footpath precisely once.

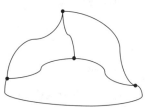

b) For a closed trail containing each footpath, what is the minimum number of footpaths that would have to be repeated?

c) The villages are joined by 4 further footpaths to a fifth village. For a closed trail containing all 10 footpaths, what is the minimum number of footpaths that would have to be repeated?

The diagram shows the length in metres of the roads in a small housing estate.

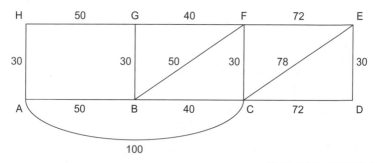

Suppose a postman, starting and finishing at A, has to travel along each of these roads. If the graph had an Eulerian trail, with the same initial and final vertices, then the postman would have to walk

> Ignore the fact that there are houses on both sides of the roads.

$$2(50 + 40 + 72) + 4 \times 30 + 50 + 78 + 100 = 672 \text{ m}$$

However, the graph has four odd vertices: A, C, E and G. The postman therefore has to walk along some roads twice, but which roads should be chosen to minimise the total distance?

In the 1960s, Mei-Ko Kwan derived an algorithm to solve all route inspection problems. At that time, he was a professor at Shandong University and so his method was popularised as the Chinese postman algorithm.

To find the shortest possible length of a continuous route which uses every edge at least once and whose initial and final vertices are the same, there are two cases to consider.

> ▶ If all the vertices of a graph have even degree then the graph has an Eulerian trail
> Any Eulerian trail is a shortest route and the shortest distance is the total of the edge weights

If there are any vertices of odd degree then Mei-Ko Kwan's algorithm is as follows.

> There will be an even number of vertices of odd degree.

Chinese postman algorithm

1 List all possible pairings of the vertices of odd degree

2 For each set of pairings:
   - Find the shortest distance between each individual pair of vertices
   - Calculate the total of these shortest distances

3 The set of pairings which gives the least possible total gives the edges which must be used twice.

If the odd vertices are A, B, C and D then there are three sets of possible pairings: {(A, B) (C, D)}, {(A, C) (B, D)} and {(A, D) (B, C)}

► If some of the vertices of a graph have odd degree then apply the Chinese postman algorithm to decide which edges to repeat
The shortest distance is given by:
Total of the original edge weights + Total of the repeated edge weights

Example 3

For the opening example of the small housing estate, find the shortest possible distance that the postman must walk.

There are 4 odd vertices: A, C, E and G. There are therefore three pairings: AC and EG, AE and CG and AG and CE.

<u>AC and EG</u>
The shortest route from A to C is ABC of length 90 m
The shortest route from E to G is EFG of length 112 m
Total = 202 m

<u>AE and CG</u>
The shortest route from A to E is ABCE of length 168 m
The shortest route from C to G is CFB or CBG of length 70 m
Total = 238 m

<u>AG and CE</u>
The shortest route from A to G is AHG or ABG of length 80 m
The shortest route from C to E is CE of length 78 m
Total = 158 m

The shortest possible distance is 672 + 158 = 830 m

In Example **3**, the roads which must be walked twice are either AB, BG and CE or AH, HG and CE. The diagram below illustrates the second of these possibilities.

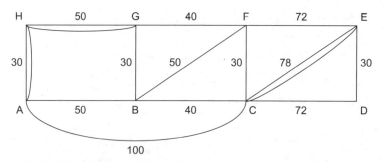

It is now straightforward to trace out a possible route for the postman. For example, ABCDEFGHACECFBGHA.

Example 4

The distances of the footpaths joining the four villages are given in kilometres. Ron, a long distance walker, intends to walk every path, starting and finishing at A.

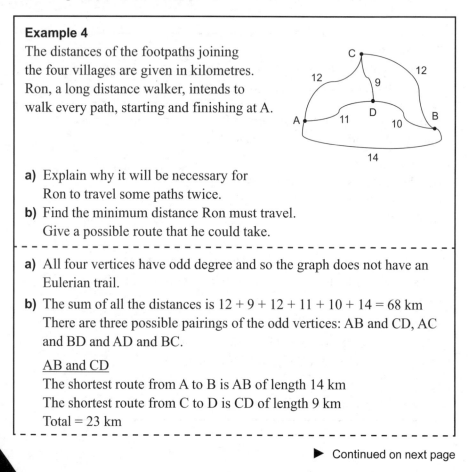

a) Explain why it will be necessary for Ron to travel some paths twice.

b) Find the minimum distance Ron must travel. Give a possible route that he could take.

- -

a) All four vertices have odd degree and so the graph does not have an Eulerian trail.

b) The sum of all the distances is $12 + 9 + 12 + 11 + 10 + 14 = 68$ km
There are three possible pairings of the odd vertices: AB and CD, AC and BD and AD and BC.

<u>AB and CD</u>
The shortest route from A to B is AB of length 14 km
The shortest route from C to D is CD of length 9 km
Total = 23 km

▶ Continued on next page

p.42

AC and BD

The shortest route from A to C is AC of length 12 km

The shortest route from B to D is BD of length 10 km

Total = 22 km

AD and BC

The shortest route from A to D is AD of length 11 km

The shortest route from B to C is BC of length 12 km

Total = 23 km

The shortest possible distance is $68 + 22 = 90$ km

A possible route, using AC and BD twice, is ABCADBDCA

You will have noticed that the Chinese postman algorithm depends upon finding the shortest distance between pairs of points. In the case of a very complicated diagram, you may need to use Dijkstra's algorithm for this.

However, it will usually be easy to see the solution by inspection.

▶ When answering an examination question on the Chinese postman algorithm, only use Dijkstra's algorithm if this has been specifically requested in the question

Exercise 4.2

1 By applying the Chinese postman algorithm to the network shown, find the shortest possible length of a closed continuous route which uses every edge at least once. The distances are in kilometres.

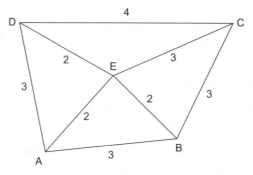

2 The diagram shows the location of a number of shop entrances at an airport terminal. The numbers on the edges show the lengths, in metres, of the walkways connecting the shop entrances.

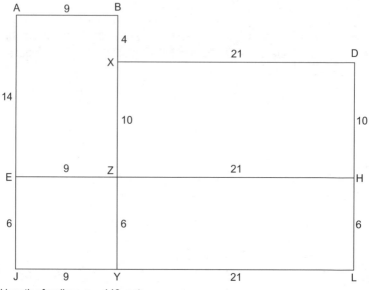

Total length of walkways = 146 metres

Leon has to walk along all of the walkways, starting and finishing at J, to empty the waste bins.

Find the length of an optimal Chinese postman route for Leon. (*6 marks*)

(AQA 2009)

3 The network shows the times, in seconds, taken by Craig to walk along walkways connecting ten hotels in Las Vegas.

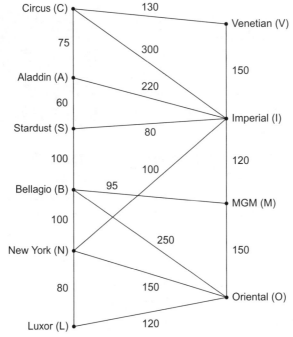

The total of all the times in the diagram is 2280 seconds.

a) i) Craig is staying at the Circus (C) and has to visit the Oriental (O). Use Dijkstra's algorithm to find the minimum time to walk from C to O. *(6 marks)*

ii) Write down the corresponding route. *(1 mark)*

b) i) Find, by inspection, the shortest time to walk from A to M. *(1 mark)*

ii) Craig intends to walk along all of the walkways. Find the minimum time for Craig to walk along every walkway and return to his starting point. *(6 marks)*

(AQA 2007)

Investigation – Route inspection

The set of instructions in your cells which determined that you developed into a human being rather than a butterfly or a giant sequoia tree is a sequence which is called your *genetic code*. This code is written in long strings of the letters A, C, G and T, which represent four different DNA-bases.

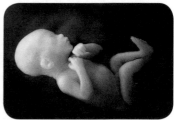

The task of obtaining the first full sequence of bases for a human being involved determining a sequence of some 6 billion letters. This remarkable task was completed on September 4th 2007.

Research
Find out more about chromosomes, genes and gene sequencing.

Physically DNA consists of two strands of bases running in opposite directions in such a way that bases always pair up in the same way: A ~ T and C ~ G. If the strands are separated then the complementary strand can be reconstructed using this unique base pairing.

$$A \_ T$$
$$T \_ A$$
$$C \_ G$$
$$G \_ C$$

One method of sequencing involves splitting DNA fragments into short single strands and finding where they match up to a long complementary DNA strand of known sequence, called a *template*. For example, suppose you were interested in strands of length three and had the template TACGGCTAG. You can obtain matches for

CTA, TAG, AGC, GCC, CCG, CGT, and GTA.

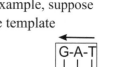

1 Which strands of length three will match to the template AGGGCTCTG?

Thus templates of length 9 can be used to match 7 strands of length 3.

2 How many DNA strands of length 3 can be matched to templates of lengths **a)** 3 **b)** 4 **c)** 5 **d)** n?

There are 4 choices for each letter of a DNA strand so there are $4 \times 4 \times 4 = 4^3 = 64$ possible strands of length 3. A template which matches all these strands, called a *universal* template, must therefore be at least 66 bases long.

3 For strands of length **i)** 2 **ii)** 4 **iii)** 5

a) How many DNA sequences are possible?

b) What is the shortest possible length of a universal template?

Consider pieces of DNA of length two which have been split into strands. Since the strands form complementary pairs it is only necessary to identify one of them in order to reconstruct the DNA fragment, say AA and not TT. Also to match a strand, a template must contain the complementary strand. For example, to match AA the template must contain TT.

AA ~ TT	AC ~ GT	AG ~ CT	AT ~ AT	CA ~ TG
CC ~ GG	CG ~ CG	GA ~ TC	GC ~ GC	TA ~ TA

4 a) What is the rule for forming pairs?

b) What strand of length three pairs with the strand ACC?

How do you find a shortest template? One clever method, based on work by the Dutch mathematician Nicolaas De Bruijn, relates the problem to that of finding a route through every edge of a particular network.

Draw the four bases as vertices of a graph and add edges to represent the complementary strand to one member of each pair. Here the first member of each pair is used: AA, AC, AG etc.

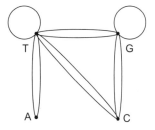

> The loop at T represents TT which is complementary to AA. The two edges connecting A and T represent AT and TA which are self-complementary.

A trail containing every edge gives a universal template. The example here gives TTATCTGCGGT. Since each edge is only used once this is a shortest universal template.

5 Repeat this method using the second member of each pair of strands: TT, GT, CT etc.

a) Draw the corresponding network.

b) Find a route around your network that passes along every edge once only and write down the corresponding shortest universal template.

Project

Choose a transport system such as your nearest underground or metro. Use the Chinese postman algorithm to find the shortest route that includes every line.

How does your 'shortest route' change when the weight of each leg of the journey is a quantity other than distance, for example, cost or time?

Consolidation

Check out

You should now be able to
- Understand the term *route inspection problem*
- Apply the Chinese postman algorithm to various problems

1 The following network shows the times, in minutes, taken by a policeman to walk along roads connecting 12 places on his beat.

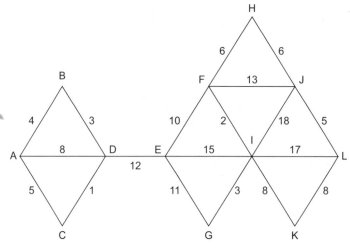

The total of all the times in the diagram is 155 minutes.

a) i) The policeman is based at A and has to visit a school situated at L. Use Dijkstra's algorithm to find the minimum time to walk from A to L. *(6 marks)*

ii) Write down the corresponding route. *(1 mark)*

b) Each day the policeman has to walk along each road at least once, starting and finishing at A.

i) For an optimal Chinese postman route, find the minimum time needed for the policeman to complete his tour. *(3 marks)*

ii) State the number of times that the vertex F would appear in a route corresponding to the minimum time. *(1 mark)*

(AQA 2005)

2 A local newspaper commissions an experienced driver to check the off-peak driving times along some of the AA-recommended routes connecting Birmingham, Cardiff, Carmarthen, Gloucester and Hereford. These journey times are shown on the network given below.

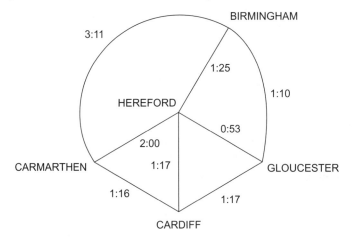

a) Find the total of all the times on the network.   (*1 mark*)

b) Explain why the driver will need to drive more than is indicated by the answer to part **a)**.   (*1 mark*)

c) Showing all your working, find the minimum driving time that the driver can expect to take to complete his task.   (*5 marks*)

d) Suggest a possible route for the driver, starting and finishing in Carmarthen, that corresponds to the minimum time.   (*2 marks*)

e) State **two** reasons why the times taken by the driver may differ from those given by the AA.   (*3 marks*)

(AQA 2007)

3 Stella is visiting Tijuana on a day trip. The diagram shows the lengths, in metres, of the roads near the bus station.

Stella leaves the bus station at A. She decides to walk along all of the roads at least once before returning to A.

a) Explain why it is not possible to start from A, travel along each road only once and return to A.

(1 mark)

b) Find the length of an optimal 'Chinese postman' route around the network, starting and finishing at A.

(5 marks)

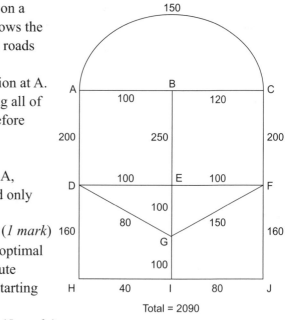

Total = 2090

c) At each of the 9 places B, C, ... J, there is a statue. Find the number of times that Stella will pass each statue if she follows her optimal route. *(2 marks)*

(AQA 2006)

4 A council is responsible for gritting main roads in a district. The network shows the main roads in the district. The number on each edge shows the length of the road, in kilometres. The gritter starts from the depot located at point A, and must drive along all the roads at least once before returning to the depot.

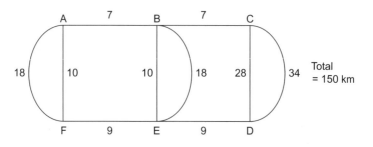

a) Find the length of an optimal Chinese postman route around the main roads in the district, starting and finishing at A. *(5 marks)*

b) Zac, a supervisor, wishes to inspect all the roads. He leaves the depot at A and finishes his inspection at his home at C.
Find the length of an optimal route for Zac. *(2 marks)*

(AQA 2011)

5 The diagram shows a network of sixteen roads on a housing estate. The number on each edge is the length, in metres, of the road. The total length of the sixteen roads is 1920 metres.

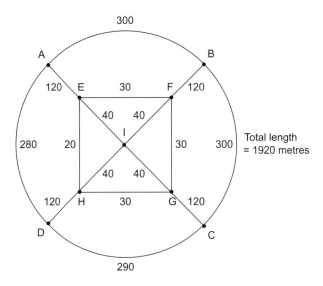

a) Chris, an ice-cream salesman, travels along each road at least once, starting and finishing at A.
Find the length of an optimal 'Chinese postman' route for Chris. *(6 marks)*

b) Pascal, a paperboy, starts at A and walks along each road at least once before finishing at D.
Find the length of an optimal route for Pascal. *(2 marks)*

c) Millie is to walk along all the roads at least once delivering leaflets. She can start her journey at any point and she can finish her journey at any point.
   i) Find the length of an optimal route for Millie. *(2 marks)*
   ii) State the points from which Millie could start in order to achieve this optimal route. *(1 mark)*

(AQA 2008)

5 Travelling salesperson problem

Industrial processing often involves a robotic arm being programmed to move between a series of sites where it carries out an operation before moving on, for example, drilling holes in a printed circuit board. To ensure that the finished product is competitively priced and profitable, this process must be carried out as efficiently as possible.

The same basic problem is faced by a travelling salesperson who has to visit a fixed set of cities but wishes to minimize the distance that he or she must travel.

> ▶ The classic **travelling salesperson problem** is to find the shortest route in a network such that every vertex is visited once

Though simple to state, the travelling salesperson problem (TSP) is notoriously difficult to solve quickly. Using brute force, you could check every possible route but the time required quickly becomes prohibitive for large scale applications. To date there is no known algorithm that can be guaranteed to find quickly the best solution.

Given its practical significance this has led to a number of major prizes being offered for an algorithm to solve the TSP.

In 1962 Proctor and Gamble ran a competition to solve the problem for just 54 cities. The then huge prize of $10 000 was won by Gerald Thompson, who happened to be an academic working on the TSP. By 2006 the largest solved problem, which was set by Bell Labs and based on the processing of a computer chip, involved visiting 85 900 'cities'.

Pragmatic solutions, which are good enough in practice, are now available for most TSPs. However, there is still considerable interest in the problem of finding exact solutions. In part, this is because of a connection with a problem known as the P v NP problem.

P v NP is one of seven mathematical problems that have become known as the Millenium Problems because they were selected for special study in the year 2000. The Clay Mathematics Institute has offered a $1 million prize for solving any **one** of the Millenium Problems.

> As of 2013, only one of the Millenium Problems has been solved. In 2010 Grigori Perelman solved the Poincare conjecture but he declined the prize!

A solution of the P v NP problem could have major significance in many fields including the logistics industry, cracking modern computer encryption and artificial intelligence.

Preparation

Before you start this chapter, you should be able to

- **Apply Prim's algorithm**

1 Find the length of a minimal spanning tree for this graph of a cube.

- **Recognise a cycle**

2 How many cycles are there that contain every vertex of the graph?

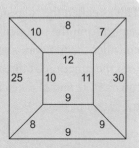

Challenge

Think of a list of places that you might like to visit: art galleries, the grounds of Premiership football clubs, local tourist attractions, etc. Set up a network with these attractions as vertices and with edges representing distances or times for journeys between them. Try to find the best possible route for a tour of all the attractions.

On the internet you will find various travelling salesperson problems concerned with travel on the London Underground.

5.1 Hamiltonian cycles

p.52

The route inspection problem studied in Chapter **4** involved finding a route such that every edge is visited. The travelling salesman problem involves finding a route such that every vertex is visited.

This diagram shows a **Hamiltonian cycle** for the graph of a tetrahedron.

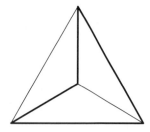

▶ A **Hamiltonian cycle** is a cycle which contains every *vertex* of a graph. It is named after the Irish mathematician Sir William Rowan Hamilton

One way of stating the travelling salesperson problem is then as follows.

▶ **The classical travelling salesperson problem**
For a given graph, find the minimum Hamiltonian cycle, that is, the Hamiltonian cycle whose edge weights have the least total

This is called the 'classical' problem because it differs in one important regard from the practical problem facing an actual salesperson. For example, consider the network shown below for four towns in Switzerland. Town A is at the junction of three valleys and travelling on the direct roads between towns B, C and D takes a long time because these roads go through steep mountain passes.

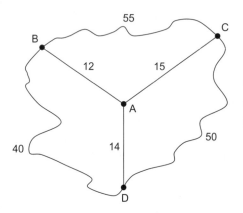

The edge weights represent the times, in minutes, to travel between the towns.

Starting from A, there are six possible Hamiltonian cycles. These are given below, together with the totals of their edge weights.

ABCDA	$12 + 55 + 50 + 14 = 131$ minutes
ABDCA	$12 + 40 + 50 + 15 = 117$ minutes
ACBDA	$15 + 55 + 40 + 14 = 124$ minutes
ACDBA	$15 + 50 + 40 + 12 = 117$ minutes
ADBCA	$14 + 40 + 55 + 15 = 124$ minutes
ADCBA	$14 + 50 + 55 + 12 = 131$ minutes

Travelling on a Hamiltonian cycle, the salesperson would therefore take at least 117 minutes. However, in practice, it would be much faster to just travel backwards and forwards on the major roads. For example, a route such as ABACADA takes just $2 \times (12 + 15 + 14) = 82$ minutes.

The problem arises because vertices cannot be repeated in a cycle. Fortunately, there is a simple solution whereby all travelling salesperson problems can be converted to the classical problem.

► **To convert the practical problem to the classical problem**
Replace the distance (weight) on each edge XY by the shortest distance between X and Y. The practical problem on the original graph is then identical to the classical problem on the new graph

For the towns in Switzerland, the new graph is as shown and all the Hamiltonian cycles have length 82, as required.

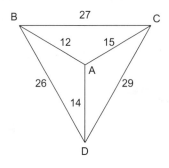

For the remainder of this Chapter you can assume that each problem is the classical travelling salesperson problem.

5.2 Nearest neighbour algorithm

Consider the task of finding a Hamiltonian cycle for the five towns marked on the above map of England. Starting from London, a "greedy" approach would be to always travel to the *nearest* town that has not yet been visited. By eye, you can see that from London you would travel to Southampton and then Bristol. Birmingham is then closer than Plymouth and so the next town is Birmingham. The cycle must then be completed by visiting Plymouth before returning to London. This approach is called the nearest neighbour algorithm.

The nearest neighbour algorithm
1 Choose any initial vertex to start the cycle
2 Find the shortest edge from the most recently chosen vertex to a vertex that has not yet been chosen
  Add this edge and new vertex to the cycle
3 Repeat Step **2** until all vertices have been chosen
4 Finally, add the edge which returns to the initial vertex

In the example given above, there are two extremely long journeys at the end of the cycle, so it is unlikely to be the best solution.

▶ A greedy approach to the travelling salesperson problem *may* produce a good solution but it rarely produces the best solution

This is a table of distances, in miles, along AA recommended routes for the five towns shown on the map.

	Bi	Br	L	P	S
Birmingham	–	88	120	203	129
Bristol	88	–	120	125	76
London	120	120	–	241	80
Plymouth	203	125	241	–	151
Southampton	129	76	80	151	–

Example 1

Apply the nearest neighbour algorithm to find a Hamiltonian cycle using the AA recommended distances shown above starting from

a) London **b)** Plymouth

----

a) The nearest town
  is Southampton   80 miles
  then Bristol   76 miles
  then Birmingham   88 miles
  then Plymouth   203 miles
  return to London   241 miles

  The cycle LSBrBi PL
  has total length   = 688 miles

b) The nearest town
  is Bristol   125 miles
  then Southampton   76 miles
  then London   80 miles
  then Birmingham   120 miles
  return to Plymouth 203 miles

  The cycle PBrSL BiP
  has total length   = 604 miles

In Example **1**, starting from London, you find a Hamiltonian cycle of length 688 miles. The shortest possible Hamiltonian cycle for these towns therefore has length 688 miles or less. The distance of 688 miles is therefore an *upper bound* for the length of a minimum Hamiltonian cycle.

▶ The length of any particular Hamiltonian cycle is an upper bound for the length of a minimum Hamiltonian cycle

However starting from Plymouth you obtain a shorter cycle of length 604 miles. The upper bound can therefore be reduced to 604 miles. It is sometimes a good idea to try to improve the upper bound further by using the nearest neighbour algorithm with other starting points. In this case, it is easy to spot a good route from the map.

▶ If you have two or more upper bounds then use the smallest one

Exercise 5.2

1 **a)** Using the map given at the start of this section, suggest a good circular route for visiting each of the towns Birmingham, Bristol, London, Plymouth and Southampton.

   b) What is the total length of your circular route?

   c) What do you now know about the upper bound for the length of a minimum Hamiltonian cycle for the five towns?

2 There is a one-way system in Manchester. Mia is parked at her base, B, in Manchester and intends to visit four other places, A, C, D and E, before returning to her base. The following table shows the distances, in kilometres, for Mia to drive between the five places A, B, C, D, E. Mia wants to keep the total distance that she drives to a minimum.

From \ To	A	B	C	D	E
A	–	1.7	1.9	1.8	2.1
B	3.1	–	2.5	1.8	3.7
C	3.1	2.9	–	2.7	4.2
D	2.0	2.8	2.1	–	2.3
E	2.2	3.6	1.9	1.7	–

   a) Find the length of tour BECDAB.   (*1 mark*)

   b) Find the length of the tour obtained by using the nearest neighbour algorithm starting from B.   (*4 marks*)

   c) Write down which of your answers to parts **a)** and **b)** would be the better upper bound for the total distance that Mia drives.   (*1 mark*)

   d) On a particular day, the council decides to reverse the one-way system. For this day, find the length of the tour obtained by using the nearest neighbour algorithm starting from B.   (*4 marks*)

(AQA 2010)

3 Angelo is visiting six famous places in Palermo: A, B, C, D, E and F. He intends to travel from one place to the next until he has visited all of the places before returning to his starting place. Due to the traffic system, the time taken to travel between two places may be different depending upon the direction travelled.

The table shows the times, in minutes, taken to travel between the six places.

From \ To	A	B	C	D	E	F
A	–	25	20	20	27	25
B	15	–	10	11	15	30
C	5	30	–	15	20	19
D	20	25	15	–	25	10
E	10	20	7	15	–	15
F	25	35	29	20	30	–

a) Give an example of a Hamiltonian cycle in this context. *(2 marks)*

b) i) Show that, if the nearest neighbour algorithm starting from F is used, the total travelling time for Angelo would be 95 minutes. *(3 marks)*

ii) Explain why your answer to **b) i)** is an upper bound for the minimum travelling time for Angelo. *(2 marks)*

c) Angelo starts from F and visits E next. He also visits B before he visits D. Find an improved upper bound for Angelo's total travelling time. *(3 marks)*

(AQA 2009)

5.3 Lower bounds

You have seen that you can find upper bounds for the minimum possible total length of a Hamiltonian cycle simply by finding particular Hamiltonian cycles. For example, **p.74** for the five towns of Section **5.2**, the cycle shown here gives an upper bound of 564 miles.

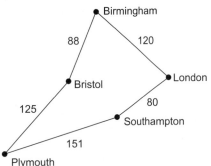

To determine if an upper bound solution is close to being the best possible you need a method of obtaining a lower bound.

> ▶ A lower bound is a number such that *all* Hamiltonian cycles for the problem have a total length of at least this number

Fortunately, there is a clever method of finding lower bounds which uses **p.22** ideas you have already met concerning spanning trees.

For the five towns, *any* Hamiltonian cycle must consist of:

- Two edges from Plymouth

- Three edges which form a spanning tree for the four towns obtained by deleting Plymouth

The two shortest edges from Plymouth are to Bristol and Southampton.

Applying Prim's algorithm to the four remaining towns gives a minimal spanning tree of total length $76 + 80 + 88 = 244$.

Therefore the two edges used in the Hamiltonian cycle must have total length of at least $125 + 151 = 276$.

Therefore the three edges used in the Hamiltonian cycle must have total length of at least 244.

A lower bound for the minimum Hamiltonian cycle is therefore given by $276 + 244 = 520$ miles.

You now know that the minimum possible total length of a Hamiltonian cycle for the five towns must lie between 520 miles and 564 miles.

This method is known as the lower bound algorithm.

The lower bound algorithm
1 Choose any vertex V
2 Find the two shortest edges from V and find the total of their lengths
3 Delete V from the graph and find the minimal spanning tree for the reduced graph
4 Find the total length of this minimal spanning tree
5 The total of the numbers found in Steps **2** and **4** is a lower bound for the total length of *any* Hamiltonian cycle for the graph

Example 2
By deleting London, apply the lower bound algorithm to the five towns of Section **5.2**

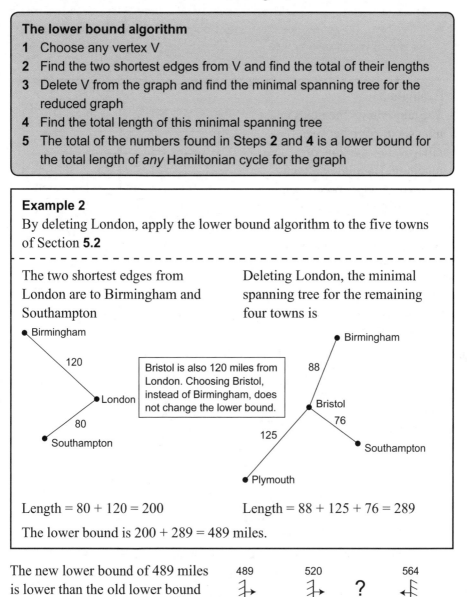

The two shortest edges from London are to Birmingham and Southampton

Bristol is also 120 miles from London. Choosing Bristol, instead of Birmingham, does not change the lower bound.

Deleting London, the minimal spanning tree for the remaining four towns is

Length = 80 + 120 = 200

Length = 88 + 125 + 76 = 289

The lower bound is 200 + 289 = 489 miles.

The new lower bound of 489 miles is lower than the old lower bound of 520 miles. Therefore it gives us no useful, new information about the length of a minimum Hamiltonian cycle.

▶ If you have two or more lower bounds then use the largest one

In rare cases you may obtain equal values for the upper and lower bounds.

> ▶ If the lower bound equals the upper bound then this is the length of the minimum Hamiltonian cycle

Example 3

The table shows the times in minutes to drive between five villages. For the time of a minimum Hamiltonian tour

a) Find an upper bound using the nearest neighbour algorithm starting at A

b) Find a lower bound by deleting E.

	A	B	C	D	E
A	–	23	13	56	42
B	23	–	22	50	61
C	13	22	–	51	51
D	56	50	51	–	17
E	42	61	51	17	–

a) ACBDEA has total length $13 + 22 + 50 + 17 + 42 = 144$

b) The two shortest edges from E, to D and to A, have total length $17 + 42 = 59$

p.32

Applying Prim's algorithm to A, B, C and D starting from A, gives:

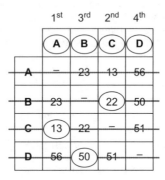

The minimum spanning tree has total length $13 + 22 + 50 = 85$
The lower bound is $59 + 85 = 144$

Since the lower bound equals the upper bound, ACBDEA *is* the Hamiltonian tour of minimum total time, that is, 144 minutes.

Exercise 5.3

1 An assembly line is used to produce five items. The times in minutes needed for each possible production changeover are as shown.

	A	B	C	D	E
A	–	165	185	65	160
B	165	–	155	115	275
C	185	155	–	205	125
D	65	115	205	–	225
E	160	275	125	225	–

All five items must be produced and the assembly line then returned to its original state. By deleting A, find a lower bound for the total of all the changeover times.

2 The table shows the times, in minutes, to travel between five places in Rome. David intends to start at one of these places and visit each one in turn before returning to his starting place. He wishes to keep his travel time to a minimum.

		B	C	P	T	V
Basilica	(B)	–	43	57	52	18
Coliseum	(C)	43	–	18	13	56
Pantheon	(P)	57	18	–	8	48
Trevi Fountain	(T)	52	13	8	–	51
Vatican	(V)	18	56	48	51	–

a) Find the total time for a tour using the nearest neighbour algorithm starting from T. *(4 marks)*

b) By deleting B, find a lower bound for the total travelling time for the minimum tour. *(5 marks)*

c) What can you deduce from parts a) and b) about the total travelling time for the minimum tour? *(2 marks)*

Investigation – The travelling salesperson problem

Here as he walked by
on the 16th of October 1843
Sir William Rowan Hamilton
in a flash of genius discovered
the fundamental formula for
quaternion multiplication

$$i^2 = j^2 = k^2 = ijk = -1$$

& cut it on a stone of this bridge

Plaque on Broom Bridge, Dublin

The symbols used by Hamilton in his graffiti do not stand for ordinary numbers but represent rotations of 3D objects. He called these symbols quaternions and spent much of his life making the case for their importance. Hamilton's work prepared the way for ideas later used in relativity and quantum mechanics but, since Hamilton's day, the use of quaternions has been largely replaced by the use of vectors.

Research
Find out more about Hamilton's contributions to mathematics.

However, the elegant and sophisticated idea of quaternions has recently found new applications in cases where the rotations are especially complicated. Nowadays, quaternions are used in both the attitude control systems of spacecraft and the computer graphics of some games involving 3D simulations.

Hamilton designed the Icosian game based upon a simple special case of his ideas. Cities were represented by the vertices of a dodecahedron and the challenge was to go 'Around the World', that is, to find a route which visits every city precisely once before returning to the start.

1 How many vertices, faces and edges are there on a dodecahedron?

Any route on the edges can be described using a sequence of the symbols L (choose the left-hand fork) and R (choose the right-hand fork). This is shown below on a 2-dimensional graph of the dodecahedron.

The first few stages in drawing a path are shown here. It can be described by the symbols LRRLL.
Can you see why a Hamiltonian tour *cannot* include these six edges?

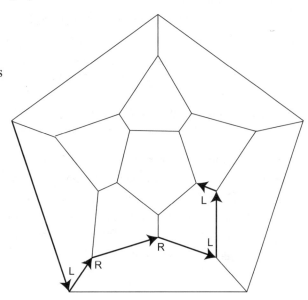

2 What would happen if a path started with LLLLL or RRRRR?

3 a) Draw any Hamiltonian tour on a copy of the graph of a dodecahedron.
   b) Starting at an arbitrarily chosen edge, use the L-R notation to describe your tour.

4 Compare your answer to **3b)** with other answers obtained by fellow students. What do you notice?

Consolidation

You should now be able to
- Understand the difference between the classical problem and the practical problem
- Apply the nearest neighbour algorithm
- Appreciate that it is not always practical to find the *best* solution for large scale problems
- Obtain bounds for the best solution

1 Peppi is a mobile hairdresser based at Chadderton (C). His day's appointments are at six places: Ashton (A), Bardsley (B), Chadderton (C), Derker (D), Edenfield (E) and Failsworth (F). He intends to travel from one place to the next until he has visited all of the places, starting and finishing at Chadderton. The following table shows the times, in minutes, taken to travel between the six places.

	A	B	C	D	E	F
Ashton (A)	–	18	14	17	31	15
Bardsley (B)	18	–	16	22	27	18
Chadderton (C)	14	16	–	13	22	15
Derker (D)	17	22	13	–	29	18
Edenfield (E)	31	27	22	29	–	30
Failsworth (F)	15	18	15	18	30	–

a) i) Use the nearest neighbour algorithm, starting and finishing at Chadderton, to find a possible route for Peppi and the total travelling time it would take. *(5 marks)*

   ii) Explain why your answer to part a) i) gives an upper bound for Peppi's minimum possible total travelling time. *(2 marks)*

b) By deleting Chadderton, find a lower bound for the minimum total travelling time. *(5 marks)*

c) Peppi thinks that he can reduce his travelling time to 100 minutes. Explain why this is impossible. *(1 mark)*

(AQA 2004)

2 a) James is solving a travelling salesperson problem.

    i) He finds the following upper bounds:

       43, 40, 43, 41, 55, 43, 43.

       Write down the best upper bound.   (*1 mark*)

    ii) He finds the following lower bounds:

       33, 40, 33, 38, 33, 38, 38.

       Write down the best lower bound.   (*1 mark*)

b) Karen is solving a different travelling salesperson problem and finds an upper bound of 55 and a lower bound of 45. Write down an interpretation of these results.   (*1 mark*)

                                  (AQA 2008)

3 Phil, a squash coach, wishes to buy some equipment for his club. In a town centre there are six shops, G, I, N, R, S and T, that sell the equipment.

The time, in seconds, to walk between each pair of shops is shown in the table.

Phil intends to check prices by visiting each of the six shops before returning to his starting point.

	G	I	N	R	S	T
G	–	81	82	86	72	76
I	81	–	80	82	68	73
N	82	80	–	84	70	74
R	86	82	84	–	74	70
S	72	68	70	74	–	64
T	76	73	74	70	64	–

a) Use the nearest neighbour algorithm starting from S to find an upper bound for Phil's minimum walking time.   (*4 marks*)

b) Write down a tour starting from N which has a total walking time equal to your answer to part **a)**.   (*1 mark*)

c) By deleting S, find a lower bound for Phil's minimum walking time.   (*5 marks*)

                                  (AQA 2010)

4 A part of London is represented by the following diagram.

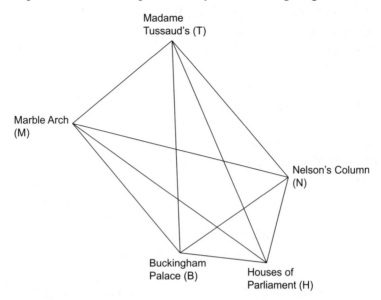

A tourist, Jess, wishes to visit five places: Nelson's Column (N), Houses of Parliament (H), Marble Arch (M), Madame Tussaud's (T) and Buckingham Palace (B).

The table shows the times, in minutes, to travel between these places. Jess wishes to keep her travelling time to a minimum.

	N	H	M	T	B
N	–	5	45	54	15
H	5	–	48	49	10
M	45	48	–	15	53
T	54	49	15	–	40
B	15	10	53	40	–

a) i) Find the travelling time for the tour HNMTBH. *(2 marks)*
  ii) Find the travelling time for Jess's tour using the nearest neighbour algorithm starting from H. *(4 marks)*
b) By deleting T, find a lower bound for the travelling time for the minimum tour. *(5 marks)*
c) Sketch a network showing the edges that give the lower bound found in part **b)** and comment on its significance. *(2 marks)*

(AQA 2007)

5 Salvadore is visiting six famous places in Barcelona: La Pedrera (L), Nou Camp (N), Olympic Village (O), Park Guell (P), Ramblas (R), and Sagrada Familia (S).

Owing to the traffic system, the time taken to travel between two places may vary according to the direction of travel.

The table shows the times, in minutes, that it will take to travel between the six places.

From \ To	L	N	O	P	R	S
La Pedrera (L)	–	35	30	30	37	35
Nou Camp (N)	25	–	20	21	25	40
Olympic Village (O)	15	40	–	25	30	29
Park Guell (P)	30	35	25	–	35	20
Ramblas (R)	20	30	17	25	–	25
Sagrada Familia (S)	25	35	29	20	30	–

a) Find the total travelling time for:

   i) the route LNOL;   *(1 mark)*

   ii) the route LONL.   *(1 mark)*

b) Give an example of a Hamiltonian cycle in the context of the above situation.   *(1 mark)*

c) Salvadore intends to travel from one place to another until he has visited all of the places before returning to his starting place.

   i) Show that, using the nearest neighbour algorithm starting from Sagrada Familia (S), the total travelling time for Salvadore is 145 minutes.   *(3 marks)*

   ii) Explain why your answer to part **c) i)** is an upper bound for the minimum travelling time for Salvadore.   *(2 marks)*

   iii) Salvadore starts from Sagrada Familia (S) and then visits Ramblas (R). Given that he visits Nou Camp (N) before Park Guell (P), find an improved upper bound for the total travelling time for Salvadore.   *(3 marks)*

                                         (AQA 2006)

6 Critical path analysis

The management of the flow of goods to meet the requirements of companies and governments is called *logistics*. To meet these requirements efficiently requires very careful planning.

As a simple example of this need for careful planning, consider the movement of containers around the world. A shipping company can earn between two thousand and five thousand dollars for transporting a full container between, say, the Far East and Europe. However, most of this trade is in one direction, from East to West. Shipping companies must therefore plan how to get the containers back to the Far East without simply losing money by having to transport empty containers.

▶ To carry out a large scale project efficiently requires careful planning. In this chapter, networks will be used to determine how projects can be completed as quickly as possible and to show how the use of manpower and resources can be optimised

The individual activities of a project can be shown in a network with directed edges indicating the order in which activities must take place. The diagram shows just a small part of the process followed when importing frozen food into the UK.

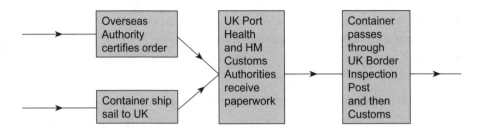

Before start this chapter, you should be able to

- **Model activities as vertices of a network with directed edges showing which activities must be completed before other activities can begin**

1   Think of various ways for a shipping company to earn money from the transportation of otherwise empty containers from West to East. What do you think happens in practice at the moment?

Consider any project involving a large number of different activities. For example, in a school or college this could be putting on a play or building a new Science block.

List the separate activities in your project and estimate the time required for each activity. Draw a network to show which activities must be completed before another activity can be started.

How would you organise the start times of each activity so as to minimise the total time required to complete your project?

6.1 Activity networks

The first stages in the analysis of a project are to:

- Break the project down into individual activities
- Estimate the expected duration of each activity
- Decide which activities must be completed before a given activity can be started.

The results of this analysis can usefully be represented in a **precedence table**. For example, consider the project of converting a room in a college into a new computer room. A possible precedence table is given below.

Activity	Duration (weeks)	Immediately preceding activities
A: Prepare room	2	–
B: Install cabling	1	–
C: Buy hardware	1	–
D: Install hardware	1	A, B, C
E: Buy software	1	C
F: Install software	1	D, E
G: Train staff	2	F

Note that activity G is preceded by *all* the other activities. However, F is its *immediate* predecessor. Likewise, G is the immediate successor of F.

▶ The activity X is an **immediate predecessor** of activity Y if Y depends on X and no other activity occurs between X and Y
▶ The activity Y is an **immediate successor** of activity X if Y depends on X and no other activity occurs between X and Y

The next stage in the analysis is to represent the activities as the vertices of a network. The vertices are drawn as boxes. The two empty boxes are for numbers which will be explained in the next section.

	D	
	1	

Activity name is D
Activity duration is 1

> ► The network should be drawn so that each activity is to the right of all its preceding activities

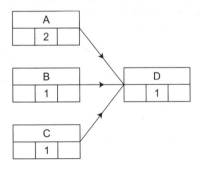

The full network diagram for the computer room project is then:

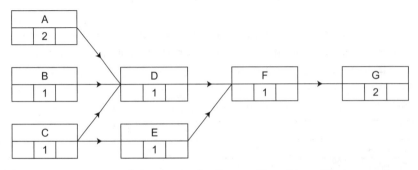

It is easy to construct activity networks for small projects. However, there are formal algorithms that a computer would follow for complex projects. An example algorithm is given below.

Network diagram algorithm
1 Draw a vertical line of boxes to represent all activities that have no immediate predecessors
2 To the right of all existing boxes draw a vertical line of boxes to represent all further activities for which all immediate predecessors are already drawn
3 Draw directed edges to represent all immediate predecessors
4 Repeat step **2** and **3** until all activities have been drawn

Exercise 6.1

1 Draw the activity network for the baking of a simple sponge cake involving the following activities.

Activity	Duration (minutes)	Immediate predecessors
A: Heat oven	6	–
B: Grease tin	0.5	–
C: Cream fat and sugar	1	–
D: Beat in eggs	0.5	C
E: Fold in flour	0.5	D
F: Put mixture in tin	0.5	B, E
G: Bake pie	12	A, F

2 The external work on a small extension has been completed. The internal work has been divided into a number of activities, as shown. Construct an activity network for the project.

Activity	Duration (days)	Immediate predecessors
A: Studding	2	–
B: Initial electrics	1	A
C: Initial plumbing	2	A
D: Plastering	3	B, C
E: Joinery	3	D
F: Final electrics	1	D
G: Final plumbing	2	D
H: Decorating	3	E, F, G

3 For the following activity network draw up a table of the activities showing their durations and immediate predecessors.

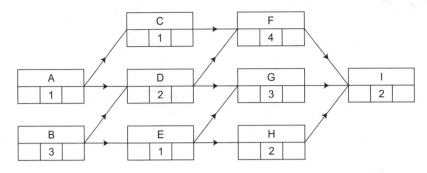

4 Draw the activity network for the baking of an apple pie involving the following activities.

Activity	Duration (minutes)	Immediate predecessors
A: Make pastry	5	–
B: Prepare apples	10	–
C: Grease tin	0.5	–
D: Chill pastry	15	A
E: Roll out pastry	2	D
F: Make pie	2	B, E
G: Bake	20	C, F

5 Draw the activity network for the following activities on a bicycle assembly line.

Activity	Duration (minutes)	Immediate predecessors
A: Prepare frame	10	–
B: Fix front wheel	5	A
C: Fix rear wheel	6	A
D: Attach chain wheel to crank	2	–
E: Fix chain wheel	2	A, D
F: Fix pedals	14	E
G: Final attachments	20	B, C, F

6.2 Early times

The next stages in the analysis of a project are to calculate the *early time* and the *late time* for each activity.

> ▶ The **early time** of an activity is its earliest possible start time

On an activity network, the early times are put into the left hand number boxes.

Example 1

Find the early times for the activities of the computer room project of Section **6.1**.

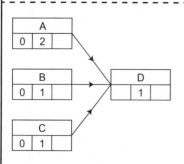

We can assume that activities A, B, and C start at time 0.

Activity D has immediate predecessors A, B, and C. Of these A is the last to finish, therefore the earliest that D can start is at time 2 (weeks).

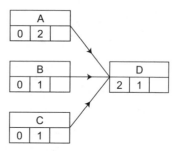

The complete diagram of early times is then as shown.

A
0	2	

B		D		F		G
0	1		2	1		3	1		4	2	

C		E
0	1		1	1	

More formally, the early time for an activity X can be found from the early times of all its immediate predecessors by applying a simple algorithm.

> **Early time algorithm**
> 1 For all immediate predecessors of X calculate:
>   Early time of preceding activity + Duration of preceding activity
> 2 The early time of X is the maximum of all these values

This rule can be applied to all activities in turn, working from the left to the right of a network.

> ► Working in the direction of the directed edges in this way is termed **making a forward pass** through the network

Example 2
Find the early time for vertex X.

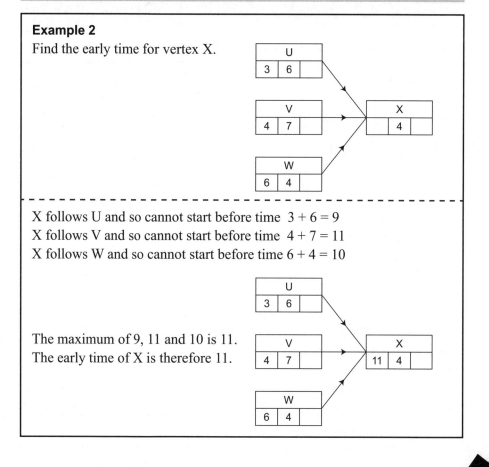

X follows U and so cannot start before time $3 + 6 = 9$
X follows V and so cannot start before time $4 + 7 = 11$
X follows W and so cannot start before time $6 + 4 = 10$

The maximum of 9, 11 and 10 is 11.
The early time of X is therefore 11.

6.3 Late times

When the early times of all activities have been calculated, the **minimum completion time** for the entire project is clearly just the largest value of

Early time + Duration

for *all* activities at the extreme right of the network.

> It is sometimes required to have only one activity at the extreme right of a network. This can be done for any network by simply adding an extra activity called *End* with a duration of 0. See question **2**, p.109

Once you have found the minimum completion time, it is then possible to calculate the late times of all other activities in such a way that the whole project is not delayed.

▶ The **late time** of an activity is its latest possible finish time

On an activity network, the late times are put into the right hand number boxes.

Example 3
Find the late times for each vertex in this activity network.

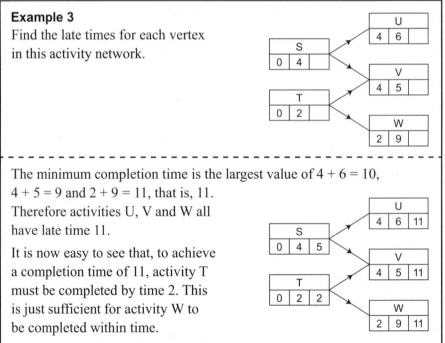

The minimum completion time is the largest value of $4 + 6 = 10$, $4 + 5 = 9$ and $2 + 9 = 11$, that is, 11.
Therefore activities U, V and W all have late time 11.

It is now easy to see that, to achieve a completion time of 11, activity T must be completed by time 2. This is just sufficient for activity W to be completed within time.

Similarly, the latest time by which S must be completed is 5, which is just sufficient for activity U to be completed within time.

More formally, the late time for an activity X can be found from the late times of all immediate successors by applying a simple algorithm.

> **Late times algorithm**
> **1** For all immediate successors of X calculate:
>   Late time of following activity – Duration of following activity
> **2** The late time of X is the minimum of all these values

This rule can be applied to all activities in turn, working from the right to the left of a network.

> ▶ Working in the opposite direction to that of the directed edges is termed **making a reverse pass** through the network

---

Example 4
Find the late time for vertex X.

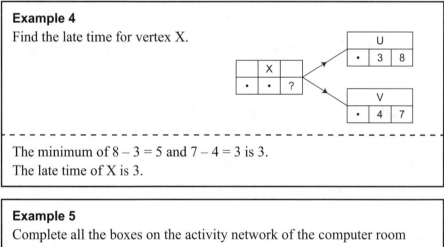

The minimum of $8 - 3 = 5$ and $7 - 4 = 3$ is 3.
The late time of X is 3.

Example 5
Complete all the boxes on the activity network of the computer room project of Section **6.1**.

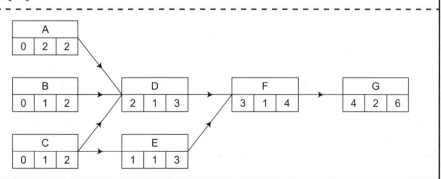

6.4 Critical activities

Consider again the activity network for the computer room project.

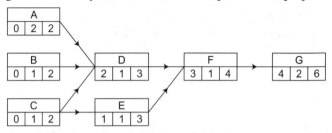

In particular, consider the timings for activity F.

Late time (4) = Early time (3) + Duration (1)

If the whole project is to be completed as rapidly as possible, then F must both start and finish as early as possible.

> ▶ A **critical activity** is an activity, such as F, with no slack in its timing

The amount of slack in an activity's timing is measured by its float

> ▶ The **float** of an activity is the value of
> Late time − Early time − Duration

The float must be greater than or equal to zero.

> ▶ An activity which is critical has float = 0
> ▶ An activity which is not critical has float > 0

Example 6

For the activities of the computer room project of Section **6.1**

a) Determine the float of each activity.

b) Identify which activities are not critical.

- -

a) The floats are: A: $2 - 0 - 2 = 0$, B: $2 - 0 - 1 = 1$, C: $2 - 0 - 1 = 1$,
  D: $3 - 1 - 2 = 0$, E: $3 - 1 - 1 = 1$, F: $4 - 1 - 3 = 0$, G: $6 - 2 - 4 = 0$

b) The non-critical activities are B, C and E which all have a positive float of 1.

You may have noticed that the critical activities for the computer room project form a path through the network.

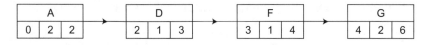

A				D				F				G		
0	2	2		2	1	3		3	1	4		4	2	6

> ▶ A **critical path** is a path through a network consisting only of critical activities

All activity networks have at least one, and sometimes more than one, critical path.

Anyone monitoring the progress of a project must pay particular attention to these critical paths in order to ensure that the project stays on schedule.

Example 7

Determine all the critical paths for the activity network shown below.

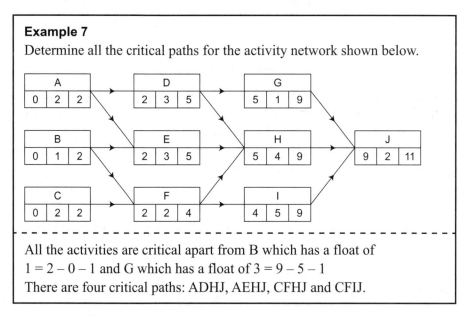

All the activities are critical apart from B which has a float of
$1 = 2 - 0 - 1$ and G which has a float of $3 = 9 - 5 - 1$
There are four critical paths: ADHJ, AEHJ, CFHJ and CFIJ.

Exercise 6.4

1 A building project is to be undertaken. The table shows the activities involved.

Activity	Immediate predecessors	Duration (weeks)
A	–	2
B	–	1
C	A	3
D	A, B	2
E	B	4
F	C	1
G	C, D, E	3
H	E	5
I	F, G	2
J	H, I	3

a) Complete an activity network for the project.   (*3 marks*)
b) Find the earliest start time for each activity.   (*2 marks*)
c) Find the latest finish time for each activity.   (*2 marks*)
d) State the minimum completion time for the building project and identify the critical paths.   (*4 marks*)

(AQA 2007)

2 The following diagram shows an activity diagram for a building project. The time needed for each activity is given in days.

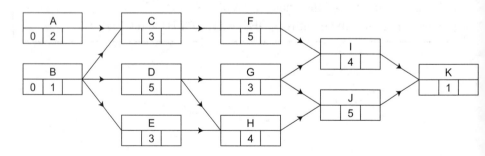

a) Complete a precedence table for the project. *(2 marks)*
b) Find the earliest start times and the latest finish times for each activity. *(4 marks)*
c) Find the critical path and state the minimum time for completion of the project. *(2 marks)*
d) Find the activity with the greatest float time and state the value of its float time. *(2 marks)*

(AQA 2007)

3 A garage is to be converted into a granny flat. The external work on the building has been completed and the inside is to be fitted out. This work has been divided into a number of activities, as shown in the table.

Activity	Immediate predecessors	Planned duration (days)
A: Studding	–	2
B: Initial electrics	A	1
C: Initial plumbing	A	1.5
D: Insulating walls	B, C	2
E: Plastering	D	2.5
F: Artexing ceilings	E	1
G: All joinery	E	3
H: Final electrics	E	1
I: Final plumbing	E	1.5
J: Decorating	F, G	1
K: Cleaning	H, I, J	1

a) Construct an activity network for the project. *(4 marks)*
b) Find the earliest start time for each activity. *(2 marks)*
c) Find the latest finish time for each activity. *(2 marks)*
d) Write down the critical activities. *(2 marks)*
e) i) Write down the float time of activity B. *(1 mark)*
  ii) State the activity with the greatest float time. *(1 mark)*
f) Both plumbing activities take twice as long as planned. Find the new completion time for the whole project. *(3 marks)*

(AQA 2007)

6.5 Cascade diagrams

In many large organisations, the results of a critical path analysis are often passed on to middle management in a particular diagrammatic form called a cascade diagram.

The main features of cascade diagrams are illustrated below for a project involving just five activities.

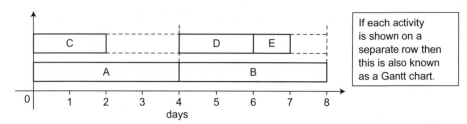

If each activity is shown on a separate row then this is also known as a Gantt chart.

Activities are often shown starting at their earliest possible time. Dashed lines show the range of times possible for an activity.

- The vertical dashed line at day 4 shows that activity C must be completed by that time. It also shows that activity D cannot start earlier than that time.
- Activity C has a float of 2 days.
- Each of activities D and E has a float of 1 day. Note that if either of these activities takes an extra day then there is no freedom in scheduling the other activity.

▶ When drawing a cascade diagram it is usually best to start by putting all the critical activities across the bottom row(s) of the diagram

A manager will decide on a particular timing of non-critical activities according to what factors, including time, are most important. For example:

- It may be prudent to do all activities as early as possible in case of unforeseen snags later in the project,
- Some activities may involve considerable investment of capital and therefore may be left as late as possible.

One particularly important aspect of the timing of non-critical activities concerns the utilisation of the workforce or of equipment. For example, a manager may try to time activities so that there is no need to hire extra workers who will then be under-employed at other stages of the work.

Example 8

The activity network for a small building project is as shown. All durations are in days.

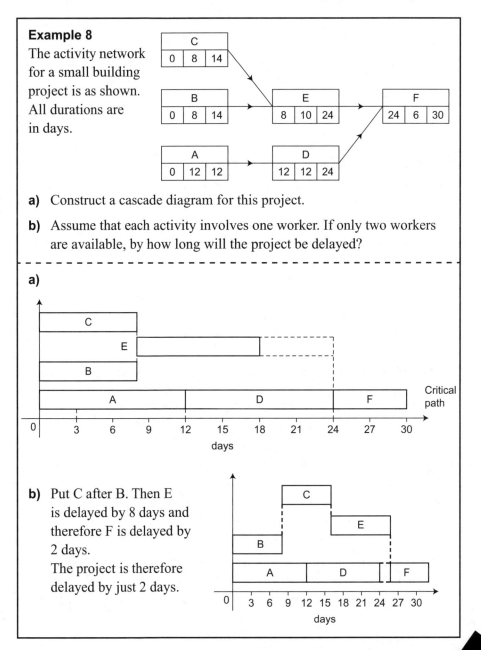

a) Construct a cascade diagram for this project.

b) Assume that each activity involves one worker. If only two workers are available, by how long will the project be delayed?

- -

a)

b) Put C after B. Then E is delayed by 8 days and therefore F is delayed by 2 days.
The project is therefore delayed by just 2 days.

Exercise 6.5

1 A small building project is to be undertaken. The time needed for each activity is given in days

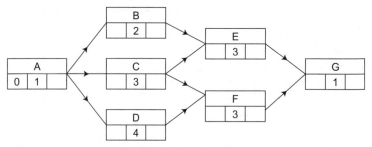

a) Find the earliest start time for each activity. *(2 marks)*
b) Find the latest finish time for each activity. *(2 marks)*
c) List the critical activities. *(2 marks)*
d) Construct a cascade diagram for the project, starting each activity as early as possible. *(4 marks)*
e) Construct a cascade diagram for the project, starting each activity as late as possible. *(2 marks)*
f) State one advantage for each of the following choices.
   i) Starting each activity as early as possible.
   ii) Starting each activity as late as possible. *(2 marks)*

2 The table shows the main activities involved in a project.

Activity	Duration (weeks)	Immediate predecessors
A	4	–
B	1	–
C	2	–
D	1	A, B
E	6	B, C
F	1	D, E

a) Construct an activity network for the project. *(4 marks)*
b) Find the earliest start time for each activity. *(2 marks)*
c) Find the latest finish time for each activity. *(2 marks)*

d) List the critical activities. *(2 marks)*

e) Construct a cascade diagram for the project. *(4 marks)*

f) If sufficient workers are employed, can the work be completed in eight weeks? *(2 marks)*

3 The cascade diagram for the launch of a new product is as shown.

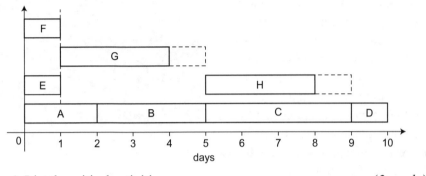

a) List the critical activities. *(2 marks)*

b) What are the two possibilities for the immediate predecessor or predecessors of activity H? *(2 marks)*

c) For one of these possibilities, construct an activity network for the project. *(4 marks)*

d) Find the earliest start time for each activity. *(2 marks)*

e) Find the latest finish time for each activity. *(2 marks)*

Investigation – Critical Path analysis

An army marches on its stomach.

Napoleon Bonaparte.

Logistical support, or the lack of it, has been crucial in many military campaigns. Its importance was exemplified in the First Gulf War (1990-91) where months of planning had resulted in the transportation of half a million troops and seven million tonnes of supplies half the way around the world. This prepared the way for what was effectively just four days of ground operations.

Critical Path Analysis differs from the other topics in this book in that its initial development was not from mathematical interest but directly because of management and military needs.

Research

Find out more about the early development of Critical Path Analysis by the Du Pont Corporation and of PERT analysis by the US Navy.

1 What is the most important difference between PERT analysis and the techniques you have studied in this chapter?

In the previous chapters of this book, you have studied the following types of problems that had been of interest to mathematicians long before many of their modern applications were known.

- Shortest set of connecting edges
- Shortest path between two vertices
- Shortest closed route containing all edges
- Shortest closed route containing all vertices

The problem covered in this final chapter was essentially that of finding a *longest* route. However, any longest route problem can easily be turned into a shortest route problem. From a mathematical point of view you can therefore think of this entire book as being about 'shortest routes'!

2 a) Explain how to turn a problem on determining a critical path into a shortest route problem.

   b) Why is it not possible to use Dijkstra's algorithm to solve a critical path problem that has been turned into a shortest route problem?

Identifying the activities on a critical path in a project is clearly important because any delay in one of these activities leads to the same delay occurring in the whole project. Conversely any reduction in the duration of an activity on a critical path has the potential to reduce the time taken to complete the whole project.

3 For the decorating project of question **3** exercise **6.4** the following changes are made, one at a time, to the duration of activities on the original critical path

   a) E is reduced from 2.5 to 0.5

   b) C is reduced from 1.5 to 1

   c) C is reduced from 1.5 to 0.5

   In each case find

   i) the reduction in the total completion time

   ii) the critical path.

> **ICT opportunity**
> Use a spreadsheet to help you investigate the effect of changing the duration of an activity on a network's total completion time.

Project

The production of a timetable for a school or college is a complex task that has to be completed on schedule each year. It depends, for example, on expected student numbers, student choices and the appointment of teaching staff. It may also be affected by the need to share teaching or facilities with nearby colleges.

Discuss your school or college's timetabling with the members of staff responsible. Draw up and analyse a network diagram for the production of such a timetable.

Consolidation

1 A consultancy company has been hired to assess the work involved in setting up an ICT system for a new school. The consultancy company has divided up the work into activities as shown in the table.

Activity	Immediate predecessors	Planned duration (weeks)
A: Decide on new system	–	1
B: Prepare ICT control room	A	2
C: Buy hardware (including delivery)	A	5
D: Buy software (including delivery)	A	2
E: Train ICT staff	B, C, D	2
F: Install cabling	C	2
G: Install hardware	E, F	1
H: Install software	G	1
I: Prepare pupil/staff data	A	5
J: Install data	H, I	1
K: Train teaching staff	H	2
L: Test system	J, K	1

a) Construct an activity network for the project. *(4 marks)*
b) Find the earliest start time for each activity. *(2 marks)*
c) Find the latest finish time for each activity. *(2 marks)*
d) List the critical activities. *(2 marks)*
e) Construct a cascade (Gantt) diagram for the project. *(4 marks)*

(AQA 2008)

2 A small construction project has an activity network as shown.

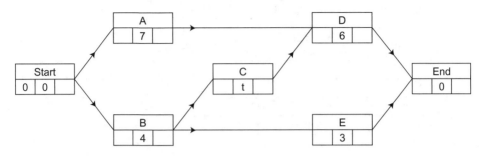

a) Complete the early and late times for the network when the duration of activity C is $t = 2$. *(2 marks)*

b) For what range of values of t is activity C critical? *(2 marks)*

(AQA 2007)

3 A construction project is to be undertaken. The table shows the activities involved.

Activity	Immediate predecessors	Duration (days)
A	–	2
B	A	5
C	A	8
D	B	8
E	B	10
F	B	4
G	C, F	7
H	D, E	4
I	G, H	3

a) Construct an activity network for the project. *(3 marks)*

b) Find the earliest start time for each activity. *(2 marks)*

c) Find the latest finish time for each activity. *(2 marks)*

d) Find the critical path. *(1 marks)*

e) State the float time for each non-critical activity. *(2 marks)*

f) Draw a cascade diagram (Gantt chart) for the project, assuming each activity starts as **late** as possible. *(4 marks)*

(AQA 2006)

4 A decorating project is to be undertaken.
The table shows the activities involved.

Activity	Immediate predecessors	Duration (days)
A	–	5
B	–	3
C	–	2
D	A, B	4
E	B, C	1
F	D	2
G	E	9
H	F, G	1
I	H	6
J	H	5
K	I, J	2

a) Construct an activity network for the project. *(3 marks)*
b) **i)** Find the earliest start time for each activity. *(2 marks)*
  ii) Find the latest finish time for each activity. *(2 marks)*
c) State the minimum completion time for the decorating project and identify the critical path. *(2 marks)*
d) Activity F takes 4 days longer than first expected.
  i) Determine the new earliest start time for activities H and I. *(2 marks)*
  ii) State the minimum delay in completing the project. *(1 mark)*

(AQA 2009)

5 The activity network for a project is shown below.

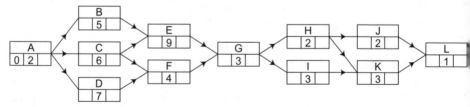

a) Find the earliest start time and the latest finish time for each activity. *(4 marks)*
b) Hence find:
  i) The critical path;
  ii) The float time for activity D. *(3 marks)*

(AQA 2011)

6 A decorating project is to be undertaken.
The time needed for each activity is given in days.

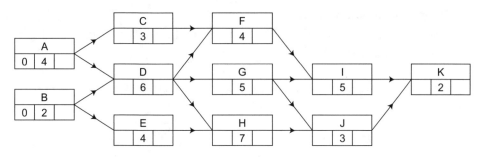

a) Find the earliest start time and the latest finish time
   for each activity. *(4 marks)*

b) Find the critical paths and state the minimum time
   for completion. *(3 marks)*

c) Draw a cascade diagram (Gantt chart) for the project,
   assuming each activity starts as early as possible. *(3 marks)*

d) Activity C takes 5 days longer than first expected.
   Determine the effect on the earliest start time for other
   activities and the minimum completion time for the
   decorating project. *(2 marks)*

(AQA 2008)

Practice Papers – data sheet

Yorkshire Sculpture Park

The map shows the location of 9 sculptures in the Yorkshire Sculpture Park during Spring 2012.

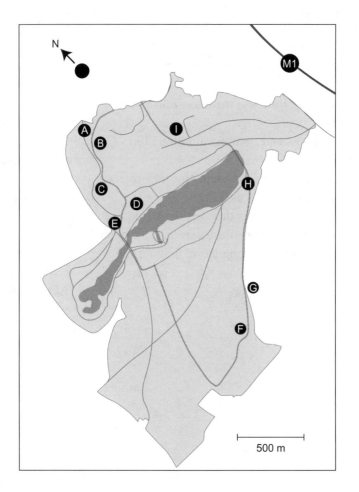

500 m

Key

A Molecule Man 1 + 1 + 1
B The Family of Man
C Seated Figures
D Promenade
E One and Other

F Basket #7
G Hanging Trees
H Seventy One Steps
I Open Air Bronze Collection

Chestnut Liqueurs

In 2012, Chestnut Liqueurs won an order to supply a chain of farm shops with a new range of products. Chestnut Liqueurs is a small family owned firm and the work had to be planned carefully to ensure that it would fit in with their existing orders. The project was divided into a number of activities as shown in the following table.

Activity	Planned duration (weeks)
A: Trial the blending process	2
B: Trial the product with tasters	4
C: Trial the product at shows	8
D: Choose glassware	1
E: Purchase glassware	2
F: Design packaging	2
G: Purchase packaging	4
H: Bulk purchase base products	2
I: Carry out mass production	2
J: Complete and deliver the order	3

Heartwood Forest

Near St Albans, in Hertfordshire, the creation of a new 858 acre native forest is well under way. Approximately 600 000 trees are being planted and miles of footpaths and bridleways are being created. Some of the existing footpaths are shown on the map.

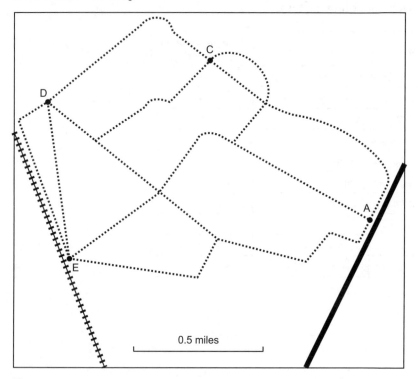

Key

+++++++++++++++++++++++++++++ Railway

▬▬▬▬▬▬▬▬▬▬▬▬▬▬▬▬ B651

A Main car park
C Hill Head Farm Drive
D Ayres End Lane
E Cheapside Bridge

Mileage chart

The table shows the approximate distances, in miles, between places in England.

	Birmingham	Brighton	Leeds	Lincoln	Liverpool	Maidstone	Manchester	Middlesbrough	Newcastle	Northampton	Norwich	Nottingham
Birmingham												
Brighton	171											
Leeds	121	257										
Lincoln	89	216	72									
Liverpool	102	277	74	140								
Maidstone	168	50	233	181	263							
Manchester	89	264	44	110	35	251						
Middlesbrough	177	318	63	123	145	283	115					
Newcastle	208	349	94	154	176	314	146	38				
Northampton	55	132	133	92	150	116	137	188	219			
Norwich	159	171	173	104	241	135	186	223	254	116		
Nottingham	54	195	74	38	102	179	71	129	160	66	119	
Sheffield	76	233	36	47	79	207	39	100	131	103	147	44

Thimbleby Technology

Thimbleby Technology won a contract to install a custom-designed accountancy system for a logistics firm. The work needed for this was divided into a number of activities which are listed below. The project was successfully completed within the 14 weeks deadline required by the contract.

Activity	Planned duration (weeks)
A: High level analysis	2
B: Install and commission hardware	2
C: Analysis of core modules	2
D: Programming core modules	3
E: Analysis of supporting modules	3
F: Programming supporting modules	4
G: Develop of management information system	2
H: Training on core modules	1
I: Full training	1

Practice Paper 1 – questions

SECTION A
Use *Yorkshire Sculpture Park* on the Data Sheet

1 The table shows the distances, to the nearest 10 metres, between some of the sculptures.

	A	B	C	D	E	I
A	–	120	450	650	720	650
B	120	–	320	510	630	600
C	450	320	–	290	280	700
D	650	510	290	–	200	620
E	720	630	280	200	–	800
I	650	600	700	620	800	–

Kate intends to meet a group of visitors at I and to visit each of sculptures A, B, C, D and E before returning to I.

a) Use the nearest neighbour algorithm, starting from I, to find an upper bound for the minimum possible travelling distance of Kate's tour. *(4 marks)*

b) Use Kruskal's algorithm, showing the order in which you select edges, to find the length of a minimum spanning tree for the graph on A, B, C, D and E. *(4 marks)*

c) By deleting I, find a lower bound for Kate's tour. *(3 marks)*

d) What can you deduce from parts a) and c) about the minimum possible travelling distance of Kate's tour? *(2 marks)*

SECTION B

Use *Chestnut Liqueurs* on the Data Sheet.

2 The project was divided into a number of activities as shown.

Activity	Immediate predecessors	Planned duration (weeks)
A: Trial the blending process	–	2
B: Trial the product with tasters	A	4
C: Trial the product at shows	A, F	8
D: Choose glassware	–	1
E: Purchase glassware	C	2
F: Design packaging	D	2
G: Purchase packaging	C	4
H: Bulk purchase base products	B	2
I: Carry out mass production	H	2
J: Complete and deliver the order	E, G, I	3

a) Complete an activity network for the project. *(3 marks)*
b) Find the earliest start time for each activity. *(2 marks)*
c) Find the latest finish time for each activity. *(2 marks)*
d) State the minimum completion time for the project and write down the critical path. *(3 marks)*
e) Construct a cascade diagram for the project. *(3 marks)*
f) For some designs, the purchasing of packaging can be reduced to 1 week. What effect would this have on the minimum completion time? *(2 marks)*

The diagram shows the walking times (in minutes) between intersection points.

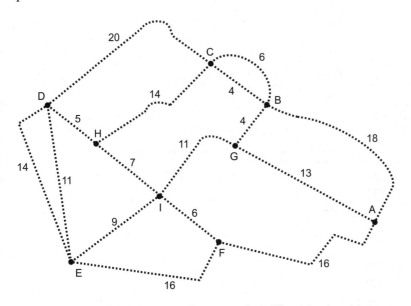

3 On a copy of the diagram above, apply Dijkstra's algorithm to obtain the smallest time from the main car park (A) to Ayres End Lane (D). Show all temporary labels. *(6 marks)*

4 The total of all the walking times shown on the diagram above is 174 minutes.
   a) Starting and ending a walk at the main car park (A), explain why it would take longer than 174 minutes to walk all of the footpaths shown above. *(1 mark)*
   b) Find the time of an optimum Chinese postman route around the network, starting and finishing at the main car park. *(5 marks)*

Practice Paper 2 – questions

Use *Mileage chart* on the Data Sheet

The network shows the distances (in miles) between places in England.

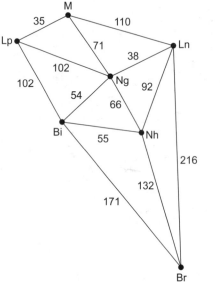

Bi Birmingham

Br Brighton

Ln Lincoln

Lp Liverpool

M Manchester

Nh Northampton

Ng Nottingham

1 On a copy of the network above, apply Dijkstra's algorithm
to obtain the shortest distance from Manchester to Brighton
using the routes shown. Show all temporary labels.   (*6 marks*)

2 The total of all the distances shown on the network above
is 1244 miles.
   a) Explain why the distance of an optimum Chinese
   postman route around the above network would be
   longer than 1244 miles.   (*1 mark*)
   b) Find the distance of an optimum Chinese postman
   route around the network.   (*5 marks*)

3 The network represents a lakeside path and the recommended walking
paths between some of the sculptures. The distances shown are in metres.

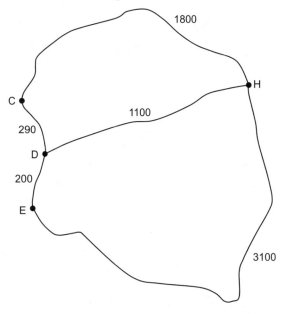

a) Write down a Hamiltonian cycle for the network shown
   above and state its length. (*2 marks*)
b) Complete a table showing the shortest distances, using
   the paths shown, between all pairs of sculptures C, D, E
   and H. (*2 marks*)
c) Use your table of distances and the nearest neighbour algorithm
   from E to find an upper bound for the minimum length of a tour
   of the network. (*3 marks*)
d) Carlos starts at sculpture E and intends to visit each of the
   other three sculptures before returning to E. Find the actual
   route that Carlos would take in order to achieve a tour of
   the same length as that found in part **c)**. (*2 marks*)

The diagram shows the walking times (in minutes) between intersection points.

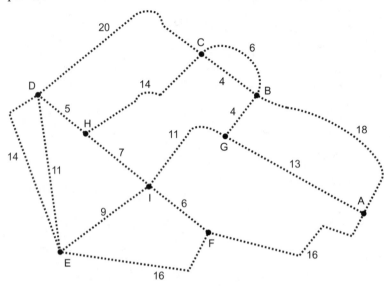

4 a) Use Prim's algorithm starting from A, showing the order in which you select the edges, to find a minimum spanning tree for the 9 intersections. *(5 marks)*

b) Draw your minimum spanning tree. *(2 marks)*

c) State the total weight of your minimum spanning tree (in minutes). *(1 mark)*

SECTION D

Use *Thimbleby Technology* on the Data Sheet.

5 An activity network for the project was as shown.

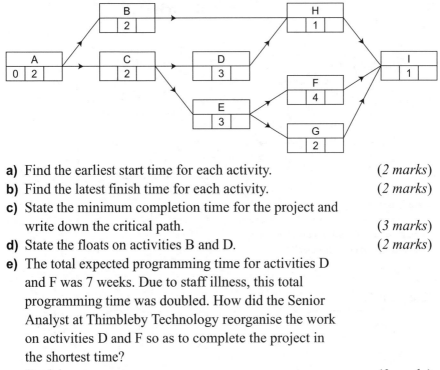

a) Find the earliest start time for each activity. *(2 marks)*

b) Find the latest finish time for each activity. *(2 marks)*

c) State the minimum completion time for the project and write down the critical path. *(3 marks)*

d) State the floats on activities B and D. *(2 marks)*

e) The total expected programming time for activities D and F was 7 weeks. Due to staff illness, this total programming time was doubled. How did the Senior Analyst at Thimbleby Technology reorganise the work on activities D and F so as to complete the project in the shortest time?
Explain your answer. *(2 marks)*

Answers

Chapter 1
Preparation

1 a) 4

b)

3 degree 0   1 degree 0,
                2 degree 1

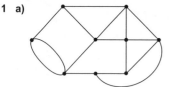

2 degree 1,   3 degree 2
1 degree 2

Challenge

"Any simple graph with six vertices either contains a triangle of joined vertices or contains three vertices not joined to each other."

This is always true.

Exercise 1.1

1 a)

b) No, there are multiple edges joining the same pair of vertices.

2 a) A, C and D are simple graphs.

b) B and E are the same
C and D are the same

3 a) $8 \times 1 + 3 \times 4 = 20$
$20 \div 2 = 10$

b) The number of edges.

c) Yes. In a simple graph each edge contributes 1 to the degrees of two different vertices.

4 a)

b) Not possible: see **Q3**

c)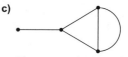

There are no simple graphs

Exercise 1.3

1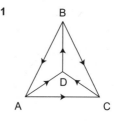

2 a)

$$
\begin{array}{c@{\quad}ccccc}
 & A & B & C & D & E \\
A & 0 & 1 & 1 & 1 & 0 \\
B & 1 & 0 & 1 & 1 & 1 \\
C & 1 & 1 & 0 & 1 & 1 \\
D & 1 & 1 & 1 & 0 & 0 \\
E & 0 & 1 & 1 & 0 & 0
\end{array}
$$

b)

To

$$
\begin{array}{c@{\quad}ccccc}
 & A & B & C & D & E \\
A & 0 & 0 & 1 & 0 & 0 \\
B & 1 & 0 & 1 & 0 & 1 \\
\text{From } C & 0 & 1 & 0 & 1 & 1 \\
D & 1 & 1 & 0 & 0 & 0 \\
E & 0 & 0 & 0 & 0 & 0
\end{array}
$$

3 a)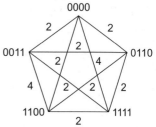

b) Errors in transmitting are likely to be detected. For example, if two code-words were confused in this example, then there would have to have been at least 2 errors.

4

	B	H	M	N	P	Pt
B	0	1	1	0	0	1
H	1	0	1	1	0	0
M	1	1	0	1	1	0
N	0	1	1	0	1	0
P	0	0	1	1	0	0
Pt	1	0	0	0	0	0

5

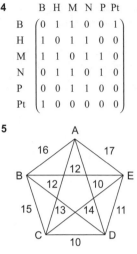

Investigation
1, 2

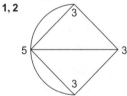

4 See Chapter 4

Consolidation questions 1

1 a) A, C   **b)** C   **c)** C
   d) A, C   **e)** B   **f)** A, B, C

2 Possible example are
   a) AB, ADCB, AEHGFB, AEHGCB
   b) ADHEA, ADHEFBA, ADCBA, ADCGFBA

3 a) i) The graph has 6 vertices.
    ii) The corresponding vertex is
       disconnected from the rest of the graph.
    iii) The graph has no multiple edges.
    iv) The graph has no loops.
    v) The edges are undirected.
    vi) The corresponding vertex has degree 3.
    vii) The graph has $14 \div 2 = 7$ edges.

b)

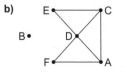

Chapter 2

Preparation
1 3
2 16
3 $700 + 740 + 770 = £2210$

Exercise 2.2
1 a) BC, CD, CE, FH, GH, AC, GI, AM
    109 metres

b)

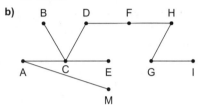

2 a) AB, FG, ED, FC, BD/AD, CD
   b) 34 miles
   c) Either AD or BD

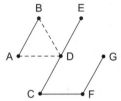

3 a) i) $10 - 1 = 9$
    ii) $n - 1$
   b) i) GI, AB, EI, BD, IJ, HJ, AF, DE, CG
    ii) 89 miles
    iii)

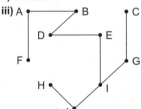

Exercise 2.3
1 a) AB, BC, AI, BD, DE, DG, DF/EF/GF, IH
   b) 84 miles
   c) Either DF or EF or GF

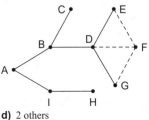

   d) 2 others

2 a) GH, GE, HJ, BE, BD, IH, DC, AC, FJ, HK

b) 117 miles

c)

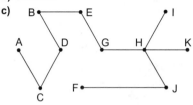

3 a) SD, SC, SA, SB, DH, HG, GF, FE, EI ,IJ, GK, KL

b) 391 metres

c)

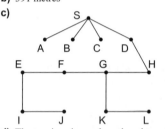

d) The tree is unique; place the edges of the minimal spanning tree in increasing cost order: 7th GF, 8th HG.

Exercise 2.4

1 a) AG, GH, GE, EF, CF/DF, BE

b)

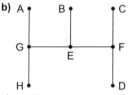

c) 23 kilometres

d) Possible reasons:

Costs may not be proportional to distances. Different villages may require different capacities.

Some roads may be unsuitable.

2 a) A-C-B $(15 + 25) \div 40 = 1$ hour

b) C-A-B $30 \div 60 + 15 \div 40 = 52.5$ minutes

c) Because the minimum connectors are different.

3 a) i) AB, BD, DE, DC, EF

ii) 15 kilometres

iii)

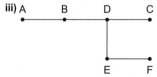

b) Possible reasons: some routes may be more expensive per kilometre or may be too disruptive or may be unsuitable.

c) i) $15 - 5 = 10$ kilometres (remove EF)

ii) 1 extra kilometre (using AC or EC)

Investigation

1 $E = 10$, $V = 8$

2 a) 7 **b)** 3

3 b) Every edge added to a tree creats a cycle.
$E - (V - 1) = E + 1 - V$

4 Let 0 be genuine

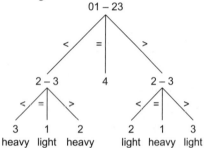

Consolidation questions 2

1 a) HI, DE, IJ, IG, AB, CG, BF, BE, FI

b) 112 minutes

c)

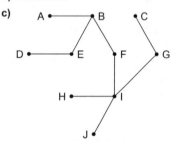

d) CG (The largest weight edge at the ends of the minimal spanning tree.)

2 a) AC, CH, FH, CE, CD/ED, GH, DB

i)

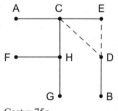

ii) Cost = 75p

b) 70p (By inspection of the edges which connect F and G to the remaining tree.)

3 **a)** 63 miles

(DE, AD, AC, EB, CF, FG or
DE, CD, AC, EB, FG, CF)

b) Either AD or CD

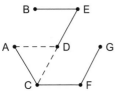

Chapter 3
Preparation
1 See p.6 and p.8

2 **a)** Designing a transport network in a congested area.

b) Transporting perishable goods.

c) Transporting non-perishable goods.

3 Almost all situations involve a combination of factors since the distance of a route affects both the cost and the time of a journey.

Exercise 3.1
1 **a)** ABCGHL or ABFGHL (7 lights)

b) Must start AE, then by inspection EF to join original solution: AEFGHL (9 lights)

2 **a)** **i)** 24 minutes   **ii)** ABCGKL

b) Combine the fastest route from A to J with the fastest from J to L.
AEFJ + JKL, 25 minutes

3 **a)** By working from K.

b) KGDA or KJGDA, 6 units; KJHEB, 6 units; KJHC or KJHEC, 5
C is the nearest.

4 **a)** **i)** 17.5 minutes   **ii)** ADFIJ

b) ACE + EHJ = 11 + 10.5 = 21.5 minutes

5 **a)** 34 minutes   **b)** DEFBAH

Investigation
1 That the processing of data by a human being and by a computer are very different activities even if they have similar outcomes.

2 Some of the algorithms that you may have found are by Fleury, Moore and Bell.

3 C is given a permanent label of 7 before the better value of 8 − 2 = 6 has been found.

4 £53.08 × 0.63 = £33.44

5 **a)** You are finding the best score for various routes.

b) The edge weights are multiplied and not added and it is a maximising problem not a minimising one.
In practice, negative logarithms are used to convert the problem into a minimising problem involving sums.

Consolidation questions 3
1 **a)** **i)** 71 minutes; 3̶2̶ 27 at F, 7̶2̶ 71 at L

ii) ABFGKL

b) AD gives 62; saving 71 − 62 = 9 mins
(30 + min time D to L = 62
20 + min time I to L = 69)

2 **a)** 1̶8̶ 17 at CH, 2̶8̶ 26 at MA
U, ST, C, CH, MA; 26 miles

b) U, CA, S, C, CH, MA; 27 miles

3 **a)** 9̶4̶ 9̶3̶ 9̶2̶ 91 at F, 145 miles

b) ABEFGHIJ   **c)** 63 miles, ABGHIJ

Chapter 4
Preparation
1 See p.5 and p.11

2 **a)** 2: C and D

b) CD is the only edge which needs to be used again. For example, ABCDEFCDFBEA

Exercise 4.1
1 **a)** 2, yes   **b)** 0, yes   **c)** 4, no   **d)** 0, yes

2 The sum of the degrees of all the vertices is twice the number of edges and therefore must be even. Since the sum over even vertices is even this implies that there must be an even number of odd vertices.

3 Consider the rooms to be vertices (with the outside as a further vertex). Consider the doorways to be edges. Then there are two odd vertices and so there cannot be a closed Eulerian trail.

4 Only A and B have odd degree and so the drawing is possible if you start at one of these vertices and finish at the other.
For example, AEDCBFECFAB

5 Yes, because all the vertices have even degree.

6 **a)** Because 4 vertices have odd degree

b) 2

c) No repeats would be necessary because all the vertices are now even.

Exercise 4.2

1 Repeat AD and BC: $22 + 3 + 3 = 28$ km

2 Repeat any pairings of E, H, X and Y:
$146 + 46 = 192$ metres

3 a) i) 465 seconds   **ii)** CASINO

  b) i) 255 seconds

     ii) Repeat CA and SM: $2280 + 75 + 195 = 2550$ seconds

Investigation

1 CAG, AGA, GAG, AGC, GCC, CCC and CCT

2 a) 1   **b)** 2   **c)** 3   **d)** $n - 2$

3 a) i) 16   **ii)** 256   **iii)** 1024

  b) i) 17   **ii)** 259   **iii)** 1028

4 a) Reverse the strand
Interchange A & T and C & G,
for example, ACC is reversed to CCA
and then becomes GGT.

  b) GGT

5 a)

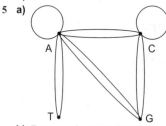

  b) For example, AATAGACGCCA

Consolidation questions 4

1 a) i) 45 minutes   **ii)** ACDEFHJL

  b) i) Only odd vertices A and L.
$155 + 45 = 200$ minutes

     ii) 3 times

2 a) 12:29

  b) There are four odd vertices and so an Eulerian trail is impossible.

  c) Repeat CnCf and BG: $12:29 + 2:26 = 14:55$

  d) One example is: CnHBGHCfGBCnCfCn

  e) Possible reasons are:
Traffic delays
The AA times are only averages

3 a) There are 4 odd vertices

  b) Repeat AI and BC: $2090 + 380 + 120 = 2590$ metres

  c) B2, C2, D3, E2, F2, G3, H1, I2, J1

4 a) Repeat AC and FD: $150 + 14 + 18 = 182$ km

  b) Repeat FD; $150 + 18 = 168$ km

5 a) Repeat AD and BC: $1920 + 260 + 270 = 2450$ metres

  b) $1920 + 270 = 2190$ metres

  c) i) Repeat BC: $1920 + 260 = 2180$ metres

     ii) B or C

Chapter 5
Preparation

1 61,

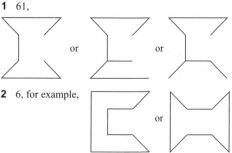

2 6, for example,

Exercise 5.2

1 a) L S P Br Bi L
(This cycle can be reversed and can start from any point.)

  b) $80 + 151 + 125 + 88 + 120 = 564$ miles

  c) The upper bound can be improved (reduced) to 564 miles

2 a) $3.7 + 1.9 + 2.7 + 2.0 + 1.7 = 12.0$ km

  b) BDACEB
$1.8 + 2.0 + 1.9 + 4.2 + 3.6 = 13.5$ km

  c) 12.0 km

  d) Swap to and from in the table or reflect the entries in the main diagonal.
BADECB, 12.1 km

3 a) Any tour, for example, ABCDEFA

  b) i) FDCABEF
$20 + 15 + 5 + 25 + 15 + 15 = 95$ mins

     ii) This is a tour but there may be another tour of smaller length.

  c) FECABDF
$30 + 7 + 5 + 25 + 11 + 10 = 88$ mins

Exercise 5.3

1 $65 + 160 + (115 + 125 + 155) = 620$ mins

2 a) TPCBVT
$8 + 18 + 43 + 18 + 51 = 138$ mins

  b) $18 + 43 + (13 + 8 + 48) = 130$ mins

  c) The minimum tour has a travel time of between 130 and 138 minutes.

Investigation

1 $V = 20$, $F = 12$, $E = 30$

2 These describe going around a face back to your starting point. Hamilton would have expressed this using algebra as $L^5 = R^5 = 1$.

3 a) For example

b) RRRLLLRLRLRRRLLLRLRL

4 Hamilton knew that algebraically all tours are the same; see **3b** Your tour may be the reverse of this (L↔R) and may start at a different point in the cycle.

Consolidation questions 5

1 a) i) CDAFBEC: $13 + 17 + 15 + 18 + 27 + 22 = 112$ mins

ii) This is a tour but there may be another tour of smaller length.

b) $13 + 14 + (15 + 17 + 18 + 27) = 104$ mins

c) It cannot be lower than a lower bound

2 a) i) 40   **ii)** 40

b) The minimum is between 45 and 55 inclusively.

3 a) STRINGS
$64 + 70 + 82 + 80 + 82 + 72 = 450$ secs

b) NGSTRIN or NIRTSGN

c) $64 + 68 + (70 + 73 + 74 + 76) = 425$ secs

4 a) i) $5 + 45 + 15 + 40 + 10 = 115$ mins

ii) HNBTMH
$5 + 15 + 40 + 15 + 48 = 123$ mins

b) $15 + 40 + (5 + 10 + 45) = 115$ mins

c) The edges form a cycle and so this is the minimum solution.

5 a) i) $35 + 20 + 15 = 70$ mins

ii) $30 + 40 + 25 = 95$ mins

b) Any cycle through all six vertices, for example, LNOPRSL

c) i) SPOLNRS
$20 + 25 + 15 + 35 + 25 + 25 = 145$ mins

ii) This is a tour but there may be another tour of smaller length.

iii) SROLNPS
$30 + 17 + 15 + 35 + 21 + 20 = 138$ mins

Chapter 6
Preparation

1 In practice, general waste and waste paper are transported back from Europe for recycling.

The container ships may travel back via India for this purpose and then continue to the Far East only partly laden. Some refrigerated containers are not suitable for transporting waste and often do return empty.

Exercise 6.1

1

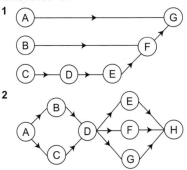

2

3

Activity	Duration	Predecessor
A	1	–
B	3	–
C	1	A
D	2	A, B
E	1	B
F	4	C, D
G	3	D, E
H	2	E
I	2	F, G, H

4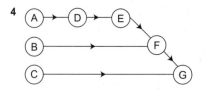

5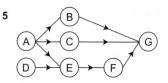

Exercise 6.4

1 a, b, c)

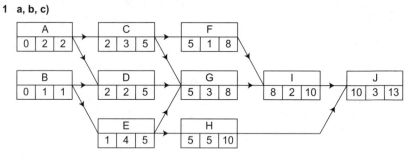

A		
0	2	2

C		
2	3	5

F		
5	1	8

B		
0	1	1

D		
2	2	5

G		
5	3	8

I		
8	2	10

J		
10	3	13

E		
1	4	5

H		
5	5	10

d) 13 weeks; ACGIJ, BEGIJ and BEHJ

2 a, b)

Activity	Immediate predecessors	Early time	Late time
A	–	0	3
B	–	0	1
C	A, B	2	6
D	B	1	6
E	B	1	6
F	C	5	11
G	D	6	10
H	D, E	6	10
I	F, G	10	15
J	G, H	10	15
K	I, J	15	16

c) BDHJK; 16 days

d) E, Float 2 days

3 a, b, c)

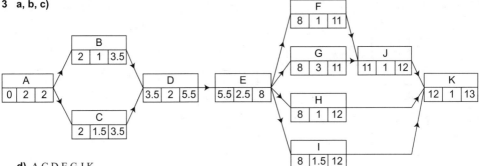

d) A,C,D,E,G,J,K

e) i) $3.5 - (2 + 1) = 0.5$ days

ii) H, $12 - (8 + 1) = 3$ days

f) 14.5 days

(Extra 1.5 days in I absorbed in its float.)

Exercise 6.5

1 a, b)

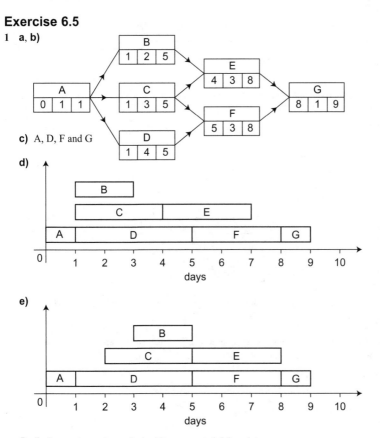

c) A, D, F and G

d)

e)

f) i) It may be easier to deal with unexpected delays later.

ii) Paying for materials and labour is delayed.

2 **a, b, c)**

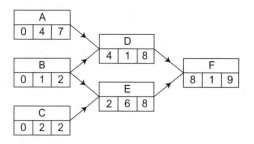

d) C, E and F.

e)

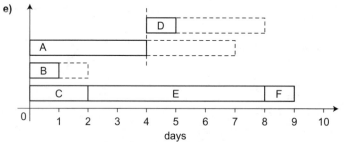

f) No. The critical path has length 9 days irrespective of how many workers are employed.

3 **a)** A, B, C and D

b) B or B and G

c, d, e)

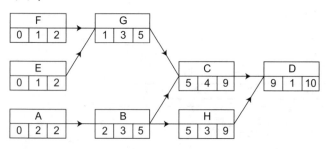

For the second possibility add an arrow from G to H; the arrow from G to C may also be removed.

Investigation

1 PERT analysis uses probabilistic estimates of all durations. This may well be appropriate for any analysis you might make since future events are never known for certain.

2 **a)** Make all the weights negative.

b) Dijkstra's algorithm only applies to networks of positive weights.

3 **a)** **i)** 2 days

ii) ACDEGJK

Consolidation questions 6

1 a, b, c)

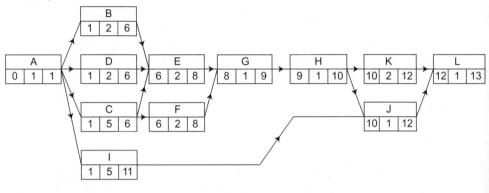

d) A, C, E, F, G, H, K, L

e)

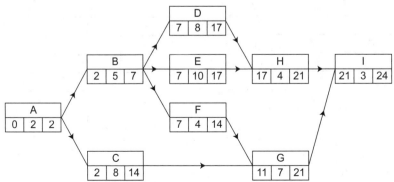

2 a) A(0, 7), B(0, 5), C(4, 7), D(7, 13), E(4, 13), End(13, 13)

b) $t \geq 3$

3 a, b, c)

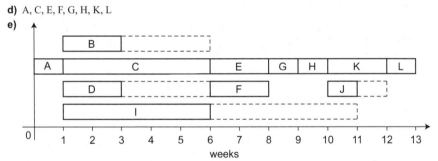

d) ABEHI

e) C(4), D(2), F(3), G(3)

f)

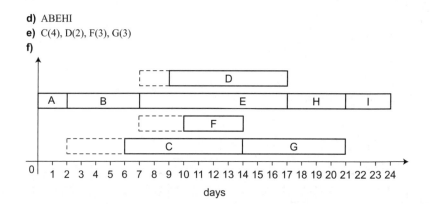

days

4 a,b)

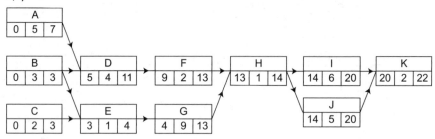

c) 22 days, BEGHIK

d) i) H(15), I(16)

ii) 2 days

5 a)

Activity	Earliest start	Latest finish
A	0	2
B	2	8
C	2	8
D	2	13
E	8	17
F	9	17
G	17	20
H	20	23
I	20	23
J	22	26
K	23	26
L	26	27

6 a)

Activity	Earliest start	Latest finish
A	0	4
B	0	4
C	4	11
D	4	10
E	2	10
F	10	15
G	10	15
H	10	17
I	15	20
J	17	20
K	20	22

b) i) ACEGIKL

ii) 13 − (2 + 7) = 4

b) ADGIK and ADHJK; 22 days

c)

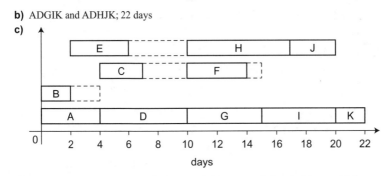

d) F starts 2 days later, I starts 1 day later. Minimum completion time is now 23 days.

Solutions Paper 1

1 a) IBACEDI; 600 + 120 + 450 + 280 + 200 + 620 = 2270 metres

b) AB, DE, CE, BC; 120 + 200 + 280 + 320 = 920 metres

c) IB + ID = 1220; 1220 + 920 = 2140 metres

d) It lies between 2140 and 2270 metres (inclusive)

2 a, b, c)

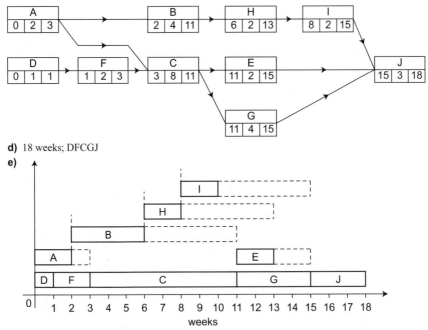

d) 18 weeks; DFCGJ

e)

f) Reduced by 2 weeks (to 16 weeks)

3 34 minutes. Show B ~~18~~ 17, D ~~41~~ 34, E ~~32~~ 31, H ~~35~~ 29, I ~~24~~ 22

4 a) There are odd vertices and so there is no Eulerian cycle.

b) AF + GH = 16 + 18, AG + FH = 13 + 13, AH + FG = 29 + 17
AG and FH must be repeated and the total time is 200 minutes.

Solutions Paper 2

1 MNgNhBr, 269 miles

Show Bi ~~137~~ 125, Br ~~325~~ ~~296~~ 269, Ln ~~110~~ 109

2 a) There are odd vertices and so there is no Eulerian cycle.

b) MLp + NgBr = 233

233 + 1244 = 1477

MLp and NgNhBr must be repeated

The total distance is 1477 miles.

3 a) CDEHC; 5390 metres

b)

	C	D	E	H
C	–	290	490	1390
D	290	–	200	1100
E	490	200	–	1300
H	1390	1100	1300	–

c) EDCHE; 3180 metres

d) EDCDHDE

4 a) AG, GB, BC, GI, IF, IH, HD, IE

b)

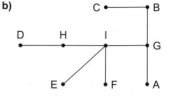

c) 59 minutes

5 a,b) A 0, 2; B 2, 10; C 2, 4; D 4, 10;

E 4, 7; F 7, 11; G 7, 11; H 7, 11;

I 11, 12

c) 12 weeks; ACEFI

d) B 6 weeks, D 3 weeks

e) Programmers were switched between D and F so as to take 8 weeks on D and 6 weeks on F. This only increased the completion time by 2 weeks because of the 3 weeks float on D and so the deadline was met.